646.78

PATROLMAN

PATROLMAN

BY
WILLIAM I. GETZ

VANTAGE PRESS
New York   Washington   Atlanta   Hollywood

Dedicated . . .
To all policemen . . . everywhere!

Contents

Author's Note

You can never find a cop when you need
one. Does your father work? No, he's a cop.
Flatfoot, fuzz, pigs!

Society in general, from the elite to the labor force, has
always entertained a resentment of authority, vocally or
silently. Resisting any form of direction or control that
would prevent their doing just about anything they
wanted. From society's youth, a dislike of parental guid-
ance, for men, the military, for all, the police . . . a
most necessary element. Control over the public is as
important as the air we breathe. No other animal in existence is as guilty as the human race of taking life, for
reasons other than self-preservation. Developing
weapons of destruction so horrendous, total annihila-
tion becomes imminent. This being a reality, the much
lesser transgressions increase. The record past and present is mute evidence to the willful lack of human conscience. As time would progress, technical knowledge
and skill would leave intelligent logic behind. Every
phase of human endeavor would suffer. War and its potential would escalate, divorce rates rise, and crime increase accordingly. Due to a lessening of restrictive
reasoning, an apathetic attitude, and an uncontrolled
drive for more freedom of expression, we would find

ourselves wallowing in complete frustration and confusion. Doing the opposite of that which is reasonable, being the criteria. Any religious or spiritual thinking is abandoned. Our gods now become lust, avarice, money and power. Laws are altered to accommodate our willful self-destruction and that of organized society. In essence, we are becoming a tribe. The educators themselves are lost in the confusion and would infect young fertile minds to "Do your own thing!" Due to self-interest, the political structure would as usual be just words. One bastion of society trying to hold the line, its effort sagging from the pressures, is the police . . . without whom chaos would reign.

Preface

By dictionary definition, one word partially describes police work: *BIZARRE*, bold, handsome, knightly, odd in manner, appearance, etc., grotesque, queer, eccentric, marked by extreme contrasts and incongruities of color, design, or style. SYN. See Fantastic. Truth of the matter is, that what policemen do is infinite, and with every new day that word is stretched. This book is about the patrol division, the beat car man, the man that comes to your aid when you dial the police number.

These men *are* the police department anywhere. What is written in most books about policemen, or presented on TV about what they do, is strictly Alice in Wonderland.

In writing this book, it was my utmost intention to stay with the truth. To put it on paper truthfully isn't easy, maybe not possible. Most people really don't want the truth. I had been told by one higher up, that the department wouldn't appreciate criticism from within. And, since I have no monies for lawyers or court proceedings, every attempt was made not to offend or criticize the powers that be.

In essence, I am forced to call this book . . . a fiction . . . so be it.

Just ask any policeman; he'll be quite frank in telling you, "No one would believe it anyhow."

Enter, if you will, another dimension: the job of a policeman—the side of life we would rather not see or do. Sit behind the wheel of a speeding squad car, become aware of what human flesh is heir to. . . .

PATROLMAN

Academy

The police academy—where men are trained to be policemen. Most people have no idea how diversified police work is. The average policeman is expected to know more about the law than lawyers. This is impossible, but expected. If you asked a policeman in your city for the directions to any given location, and he didn't know, you would think him to be stupid. People expect policemen to know just about everything.

The academy was very strict. You must be well-disciplined to learn much in a short span of time. Some of the subjects were law, arrest procedures, first aid, patrol procedures, humanities, a multitude of reports, from disorderly complaint forms to bonding receipts, the governmental structure of our land, judo, shooting techniques of various weapons, shoot-out situations, riot control, traffic reports, ticket writing, and ordinances. Also, squadrol operation, how to deliver a baby, investigative techniques, court procedures, semantics and racial understanding. The instructor thrust his finger at one of the black recruits. "What will you do if a man calls you a dirty nigger?" Taken by surprise, the recruit stammered, "I, I, I'll blow him away!" His response was emotional and you could see he was angered. "No you won't," the instructor countered. "You will ignore what he said and remain calm, doing your job in a legal and professional manner." As a

1

policeman, you give up your racial background; your race is that of a policeman, no other. Tolerance must prevail for you to perform your job. At the scene of any disturbance, even a union dispute, you are not allowed to have a point of view, or take sides.

During the academy training period, we were to see dozens of training films on various subjects. Lectures and note taking every day, a test every week, and all the time trying to maintain an average of 70. Anything less would wash you out. It was hectic and you couldn't retain it all, but I think most of the men enjoyed it.

Finally, graduation, and you were assigned to a district or area, where the training and practical application would blend. For the first few months you would be on probation. Your ability, performance, or any unusual quirks would be duly noted by the field training officer. Stress situations can reveal latent psychological imbalances.

Every phase of the Academy training would be tempered by the now-present situations. You were only a policeman . . . not God. Everybody who broke the law wouldn't be arrested, and a marriage of fifteen or twenty years couldn't be saved by you in twenty minutes. The husband and wife now standing toe to toe damning each other would probably be lovers tomorrow. In most cases, simply separating these arguing lovebirds would suffice. By contrast, a domestic disturbance where emotions ran high could be dangerous. A jealous husband or wife might kill, as they saw their world crumbling before their eyes.

Working the street was the real thing, and, for a new man, keeping his mouth shut and eyes open was good advice. With all the invaluable knowledge learned at the Academy, there was more to know . . . much more. Time would pass and you encountered different situations. The realization became apparent, no matter how long you were on the job; you would never see them all. Every day there was a lesson to be learned. You were becoming a civilian soldier, earning your distinguished title . . . Patrolman.

Roll Call

Hot! Damn, it was hot. Local traffic was screwed up, as usual: absent-minded women, the long-haired kids whose lack of discipline spilled into their driving habits, the oldsters, senses failing, forcing them to drive in an overly cautious manner, creating more hazards.

Sweat trickled down my temples. The combination of heat, anxiety, and woolen trousers was winning. My armpits were sweating profusely, the fresh police shirt wilting accordingly.

Before me stretched the expressway, almost at a standstill. Stop and Go, Stop and Go, five miles an hour. The only thing moving fast was time. Late again, I was almost always late for roll call, or just barely making it. Probably because I wasn't too anxious to get there. Safer to park in the station parking lot, even if the car got scratched or dented, at least after work it would be there. I bounded up the stairs, spirits soaring, but the next half hour would diminish that. The troops were milling around, talking and joking. Some just sitting there resigned to their fate. Fortunately, I have a fantastic disposition, usually in a good mood and anxious to smile. "Why so happy, Bill? You must know something we don't." "It's quite simple; I'm happy because I know it can only last eight hours—then when it's over, I'm happy its over." Guess I had psyched myself out so I could cope with the job.

"Fall in!" the captain said as he walked into the

roll-call room carrying what's known as the captain's book, which contained the daily notices and assignments. One or two sergeants were usually present, sometimes a lieutenant or guest speaker. "Dress right Dress! Ten Shun!" The captain, now at the podium, called out the men's names and assignments. These accounted for, the captain and a sergeant strode past the two files of men, checking their uniforms and general appearance. "Very good, have a seat." Several benches in the room were filled; some men stood. Death notices of retired policemen or relatives were given. Vandals harassing a particular location, an incident where some patrolman goofed in spades. The whole atmosphere of roll call was governed by the captain's disposition. "Any comments?" Usually not. Book under his arm, the captain left the room. The senior sergeant stepped to the podium. "Take some auto's"—usually nine or ten additional license numbers of the most recent steals. What followed could be humorous, serious, boring, informative, or completely stupid! The rapport between the sergeants and the men left a lot to be desired. Rarely were we commended; some index for something was always low. "Hit the street!" We ambled down to the radio room, got a portable police radio, then into the parking lot to find our beat car. All the cars on the third watch were two-man. Policemen are like snowflakes—no two alike.

It's been my pleasure to work with many that were highly intelligent, aggressive, understanding and compassionate. One or two, I thought, should be physically contained, or at least needed psychiatric help.

Being a cop requires a flexibility most people cannot endure. One minute you're speeding a sick or injured kid to a hospital, the next, some drunken bastard is trying to kick your balls off. For maybe an hour you're on peaceful patrol, then the radio tells you he's being pursued at a high rate of speed into your district. There he is! Flying through the intersection, maybe seventy miles an hour. We've got to get that crazy bastard before he kills somebody. The inertia of sudden acceleration glues you to the seat back. Now the siren is screaming so loud you can't hear the radio. This is the chase! Every one is the first. Tires moaning their strain at corners, lights flashing, siren and radio blaring. The frantic capture, the mandatory paperwork.

Your next assignment, "Loud stereo, second floor rear, complainant, Mr. Fribbish on the first." Would you believe a sick canary? That any marriage lasts for policemen is a small miracle. The different hours, frustrations, tedium, emotional fatigue, control over your own kids lacking because you're not home like most fathers. When you're doing *for*, you're "officer," when you're doing *to*, you're a pig, a bastard, police brutality! Damned if you do, damned if you don't. The only contact most people have with the police is a traffic ticket. This is extremely unfortunate. Nobody likes to get a ticket. One guy told me I should be out catching a burglar. I told him I caught one yesterday and he, the burglar, told me I should be out catching a traffic violator. Can't please everyone! Policemen who drink don't do it as a habit—it's therapy.

The name of the game is a good partner. Someone you can depend on, aggressive at the right time, logical, and most important, flexible, with a sense of humor. Ski was such a policeman. We caught a three-man robbery-rape team because we worked well together. These mopes would rob women on the street at the point of a sawed-off shotgun, then rape the younger ones. They were operating for quite a while. Unmarked detective cars and other units couldn't bring 'em down. The patrol division did! Were it not for dedicated street patrolmen you wouldn't be safe inside a police station! Policemen arrest thousands of perpetrators—most, repeaters. But prosecution is the weak link. Our laws are an incentive to crime.

Patrol

Patrol in our district: A conglomeration of shops and stores, some boarded up, many covered by metal grills; or bars—a profusion of taverns and people of every description.

My partner stoically gazed forward as he urged the squad through the ever present traffic. We swung through the park and onto a main street, with its flashing signs and lights belying the potential treachery. In the failing daylight some young boys played basketball amidst the broken glass in an alley. A green Dodge turned left at the intersection, where the sign told him not to. As my partner spoke to the driver, two boys ambled over to the squad. When asked if policemen were good, they answered, "Yes, policemen protect us."

There is always hope with the young, thank you Carlos and Renaldi. Every time I would start to really think our efforts were in vain, some incident or person would let me know we were desperately needed. For every punk with a knife or gun we arrested, there are thousands of good kids, many with a friendly smile, who would cross the street just to say, "Hello, Officer, how are you?" People have even thanked me after receiving a ticket; perhaps they realized a new awareness in their driving might save their life, or someone else's.

We parked near a main intersection to observe the traffic. During these pauses you could collect your thoughts, or try to relax. Lighting up a cigarette, I sat back and vacantly watched the smoke trail upwards, then disappear. The police radio was incessantly assigning jobs to other units, the complex myriad of illegal human endeavors. The traffic moved both ways in a steady stream, in most cases, people seeking to vent their frustrations . . . the usual weekend traffic. One drunk that had apparently gotten an early start, stumbled by, oblivious to that around him. Longhaired kids wearing flared blue jeans walked by, laughing with gay abandon. Middle-aged women, arms laden with groceries, hurried home to fix supper. Sounds galore, car horns, sirens, traffic, kids and barking dogs. The forever police radio—damage to property, sick person, kids playing ball where they shouldn't, disturbances, down drunks, traffic accidents . . . "Stand By" . . . Every assignment preceded by a beat car number. We listened intently for ours. "Overdose, St. Christopher Hospital." "10-4"—we were in business. My partner shifted to drive and I shuffled through the various forms looking for the one we would need. Policemen are in hospitals quite frequently, pursuant to investigations, and, over the years I had seen many nurses. Nurses all seem to share a rather pompous attitude, probably because they could distinguish an oral thermometer from a rectal type when most other people can't. This nurse was no exception. With that air of superior indifference, she spoke, sounding like a telephone company recording.

"His name is Angel Rodriguez, a friend brought him in and left." Handing me the emergency admission form, she added, "Don't forget to sign it." She turned and briskly walked out of the emergency room, her snow white, starched uniform rustling from its stiffness. *Probably going to sort some thermometers*, I thought.

Angel was lying on an emergency room bed, eyes half open—seeing nothing, his whole being in a dimension no one knew. The brown stained fingers indicated he probably started with smoking marijuana, the drug cigarette many pseudo-intellectuals tell kids is safe to smoke. The fact that all hard narcotic users started with smoking pot seems to have eluded their deductive reasoning. During my youth, I knew some guys that smoked pot, because they thought it made them cool. Some actually lived to the ripe old age of thirty-five. One thing for sure, they are all cool now . . . just as cool as a body ever gets.

Angel's arms both bore the needle marks that were responsible for his half-dead condition. "Angel, this is the police!" We could have shouted. Angel's senses were filled with sounds and sights that blocked all others. Even if he were coherent, he wouldn't tell the police anything—probably too cool to talk to the pigs. It would all be just lies anyway. Transcribing the information from the emergency room form was the usual routine. Overdose victims are getting as common as colds, and, at this stage of the game, we're not able to stop colds, either. Angel's condition wasn't considered to be critical by the doctor, but, if he did die, a wagon crew would be summoned for removal. And they would use an identical form, just "X" a different box, writing in a different narrative. No flowery epitaphs for junkies. After all, they're just passing through society, more like being on . . . a short trip.

All those who had been separated from loved ones, either through life's edicts or death of their spouse, are handled by the police shortly after their last hours. Millions of such older, lonely people, living on memories of happier past times are to be found in drab one-room apartments, or old houses, decrepit from lack of care once lovingly given during the owner's younger years. For these older people living alone to prove their independence, the visits of relatives and friends became less frequent as they, themselves, would pass on. Just sitting there staring out a window or sitting in an old rocking chair, staring at past visions, awaiting death. Loneliness, their only guest. Usually having just enough money to pay for rent and food to sustain life. Some are actually surviving on food intended for dogs. The clothes they wear are faded from countless washings. Alone . . . save their memories. Perhaps a faithful pet, itself suffering from arthritis or other forms of infirmity brought about by old age. In time, some policeman would be shuffling through their personal effects, hoping to find among the yellowed papers a name and address of a relative or friend who could be notified to make the final arrangements. Most times there were photographs and pictures of the victim's early days. Bonnets, high collars and, in the background, a horse and buggy, standing alongside a wooden sidewalk. Old letters written by people long since passed. Prayer beads and religious items usually keeping company with a much-used Bible. In the homes, all the furnishings would undoubtedly be as old as the occupant—antique. In the one-room apartments, everything would be singular. A cheap wind-up alarm clock, one second-hand wooden chair and table. The inevitable table radio with its cracked plastic housing. All the personal effects contained in a shoebox or old battered suitcase.

I remember one case involving a man who had lived alone in such an apartment. The man who had worked as a watchman, was found in a sitting position on the floor. His back against the wall, head down, a small hole in his forehead where the .38 caliber bullet had entered. His hand still holding the gun, thumb curled around the trigger. On a table in the apartment stood some prescription bottles, his eyeglasses and a half empty quart beer bottle. Next to the beer bottle was a glass, still containing about an ounce of the amber liquid. You could see he had been reading a paperback cowboy story. The book still open, a marker in place. I picked up the book and read a few paragraphs, wondering if he might have read something that induced him to make that terrible decision to take his own life. There was no connection. Apparently, his will to live was overcome by ill health and loneliness. He had simply had enough. In the silence of this setting, I looked at him and the drab surroundings. I wondered how many more there must be in such a similar pathetic situation. Ill, alone, no laughter, no new horizons to conquer, just the very desolate, waiting for the inevitable end. For this poor soul, the wait was too long. What did he think in his last moments? Was it his physical discomfort or just the loneliness . . . or both? As a young man, in his wildest imagination did he ever dream it would end this way? I pondered these thoughts until the wagon men arrived. Here was the death of a total stranger to me, but somehow I felt the loss. In a small way, I could now understand the sad, lonely existence of all who were alone and forgotten. Later that evening, I would look at my wife and children and realize how fortunate I was.

We responded to a domestic disturbance call, trudging up a steep stairway to reach the apartment situated above a tavern. At the top we were met by a young Latin, who related his neighbor was beating his own wife. With widened eyes, the Latin described how she screamed and begged for mercy. As he spoke, the drunken wife-beater approached. "What the fuck do you guys want?" he slobbered. My partner said, "Keep an eye on him, I'll talk to his wife." The husband stood there glaring at me defiantly. In a minute my partner returned. "Boy, he really did a job on her. Her whole face is puffed up. Go take a look." The job had taught me that dead bodies and other unpleasant scenes leave an indelible picture on your mind. "I'll take your word for it, Tom," I said. "You're under arrest, let's go," Tom told the husband. As he spoke, he grabbed the husband's right arm . . . "I'm not going anywhere," the drunk said, leaning back. Without thinking, I grabbed our resister by the front of his jacket. "You're going to the hospital, you son of a bitch!" Maybe this wasn't book procedure, but I can't stand so-called tough guys that would beat on someone who was defenseless. I think my first impulse was to throw this rotten bastard down the stairs. Tom, seeing my anger, wouldn't release his hold. There we were, at the top of that steep stairway. Me, wanting to throw our prisoner down the stairs and Tom holding on trying to prevent it. By now, I was down one or two stairs, with Tom and the drunk above me. Definitely the wrong place to be. Tom couldn't resist my pulling and the drunk's weight. He let go. I swung around and with my left hand grabbed the bannister. But the inertia of the drunk's weight, plus my pulling, was too much. The bastard grabbed my jacket on the way down and the bannister pulled right out of the wall. Down we both went, not touching anything in between. Of course, I was first to arrive, landing on my back, our prisoner following, right on top of me. There we lay in a tangled heap. "Oh, my God!" the Latin exclaimed, "that poor policeman." It all happened so fast it was unreal. I lay there wondering what was broken. The drunk started moaning his leg was broken. Then I realized I couldn't breathe. The police radio I was wearing on my belt had slid behind me on the way down and upon landing on it had knocked the wind out of me. Struggling to my feet, I fought desperately to get my breath. By now, Tom was down the stairs. "What's wrong? Are you all right?" Finally managing to suck in some air, I barely whispered, "I can't breathe." All this time our prisoner was still moaning, "My leg is broken." You should have seen Tom's expression. He didn't know what to do next. Me gasping for air and the drunk repeating his leg was broken. It was a terrific fall and a small miracle that either one of us didn't break our backs. In a few minutes, my breathing was back to normal, and we helped the prisoner up. To our surprise, the dumb bastard wasn't hurt at all, I had gotten the worst of that fall and even today something in my chest area occasionally pops out under strain. But I guess it's not too serious, it goes back by itself. After all these years, and knowing better, I could still lose my temper with enough provocation. What the hell! Nobody's perfect.

"Some dirty person stole my shopping cart!" "Can you describe it?" His description was that of a chain-store type, the type they definitely don't sell. Our complainant had actually called the police to report the theft of a shopping cart he himself had evidently stolen. Believe me, that's really not unusual. He invited us upstairs, where we could write our report. As we climbed the stairs, we noticed two hoses that led from the basement. The entrance to his flat has a storm door made up of little framed glass panels. One panel was broken, allowing passage of the two hoses, which were surrounded by jagged glass. First of all, removal of that particular pane would have been simple. Secondly, the storm door was open. My partner had a good sense of humor and was easily brought to hysterics. I could get him laughing without much effort. The bit about the shopping cart, and now the hose through the pane, had gotten him started. Once inside the flat, we could see that the two hoses were to facilitate a water-cooled air conditioner—standing two feet from the sink.

There was an assortment of junk strewn all over. Not a clear horizontal in the place where we might write our report. Our complainant kept rattling from one subject to another, never bothering to finish any. To top it off, he had one of those beautifully comical faces, capable of limitless expressions. As he continued, arms flailing, exaggerated expressions, and falsetto voice, Tom couldn't contain himself. Face red from trying to stifle his laughter, he turned away. By now, the scene had me going also. As we pretended to be looking at the junk-littered floor, we both laughed until we could regain control. Everything about the situation appeared to be humorous. The water-cooled air conditioner, which needed only four feet of hose, not a hundred and eighty. Breaking the glass panel, instead of removing it. His demeanor and funny antics. Even his laughing with us, and not knowing why. We weren't being unkind, it was a truly funny, human situation. I had better control than Tom and, after ascertaining the facts, which were dubious, we started to leave. Grabbing the storm door, I felt a slight sensation, like that of getting cut. Cautioning Tom, I said, "Watch out for the door, I almost cut myself." Without hesitation, our comical host asked, "On the hose?" Neither Tom nor I had that much control and we just about fell down the stairs laughing.

Dispatcher

The catalyst . . . heart of the patrol division. Patrolmen
who serve as dispatchers make the whole thing work.
Without their expertise, we would be merely driving
around in circles. The appearance of police vehicles on
patrol is theoretically for deterrence of potential crime.
Effectiveness of patrol is an unknown factor. Like most
medicine we take, the assumption is that it helps. However, ninety per cent of actual fruitful police service is
via the dispatcher, sometimes called the squad operator.
Calls for service from the public go directly to the radio
room wherein the dispatcher, using his street knowledge, appraises the situation, dispatching patrol vehicles, as is necessary. No small task. Many times human
lives are at stake, both civilian and police. In a chase
situation, the dispatcher must advise all the vehicles to
the direction of travel, what, where, and why. Direct
vehicles not in pursuit to locations of convergence.

The dispatcher's heavy rapid breathing lets us
know that he, himself, is caught up in the exhilaration
of an exciting situation. It is not uncommon for dispatchers to succumb to heart attacks. During the riots,
their responsibility was horrendous. Numbers of locations, beats, supervisory numbers, time differences, and
now helicopters, manned by policemen. Marches, pro-
testers, or any large group moving in unpredictable directions create additional difficulties for the dis-

patcher. In these situations, traffic must be stopped or re-routed on a spontaneous basis. The job these radio operators do is simply phenomenal. Every situation is different and calls for an immediate corrective response. Despite the pressure on these men, they still manage to maintain a sense of humor. From time to time they and the beat car men will exchange humorous quips. A little levity never hurts. Quite often some patrolman involved in a chase or other dangerous situation will, because of his excitement, fail to keep the dispatcher informed as to the situation. Wanting to assist the officer to the best of his ability, but hampered by a lack of information, the dispatcher will anxiously ask, "Where are you at? What direction are you traveling? Are they armed?" or any one of a half dozen different queries to ascertain necessary assistance. Sometimes repeating a question several times with escalating anxiety. When no response is forthcoming, you could hear the frustration in the dispatcher's voice. They become "uptight." To vent their frustrations or anxieties, they will inject some humor into the less serious assignments.

A domestic disturbance might come over the air as "Save the marriage, 1204 N. Ohio, 1st, Rear." Or, in a situation where kids are playing ball in an area laden with windows and should be stopped, the dispatcher might say, "Referee the game, 603 S. Elm." On midnights, when calls during the winter months are less frequent, an occasional short quiz might be in order—"Who won the pennant in 1935?" or, "Who had the most home runs for the Cardinals in 1938!" At least being on the street, the beat man's day has variety. No two days even remotely similar. For the dispatchers, day after day, hour after hour, they are confined to their consoles. Even the paper work is demanding when it is busy. Time cards, assignment cards, checks on license plate numbers, warrant checks on suspects, even personal service like, "Officer Smith, call your wife at home; no emergency." Some calls only suggesting danger are emphasized, "Use caution, possible weapon." Or, "He's a police fighter." Alerting a beat man to a situation he may not have known about. "Be careful, they sniped at the police at that location two days ago."

With over ten thousand policemen on the department, few would ever get to meet the dispatchers personally. But there is no doubt that the men on the street owe their well-being, even their lives, to the policeman simply known as the dispatcher. To these men we are deeply grateful. Though we may never meet, I know the troops all share a respect and warmth for the heart of the patrol division—the dispatchers.

Wagons

One of the most uncomfortable conveyances ever made is the squadrol, commonly known as the wagon. It is a beautiful sight, arriving when you have unruly prisoners. But bouncing around in one for eight hours is nothing to look forward to. The wagon is used most extensively to transport prisoners, sick people, drunks, injured people, pregnant women, dead people, or to convey policemen to the scene of big disasters or riots.

Because of the heavy-duty suspension required of such a vehicle, they ride quite hard. If you drove over a dime, you would probably know it. Having a high overhead causes them to be top heavy and they sway on turns, like a drunk off balance. Considering the abuse they take being driven around the clock, they are pretty strong. Men who work these vehicles on a steady basis get the label "wagon man."

Occasionally, I worked the wagon and it was a welcome relief from the beat car, but to work it steadily was not for me—too many dead bodies. These vehicles handle everything from an occasional newborn baby to dead bodies, plus everything in between. No other vehicle made can boast that spectrum! Being a wagon man calls for a strong stomach.

I remember an incident once when I was working a one-man beat car. My assignment was to check on the well-being of an elderly recluse. It was a hot day in

August and the pungent odor at the address given was unmistakably that of a D.O.A. If there were any doubts, the swarming flies inside the apartment windows immediately dispelled them. Most people have never had the misfortune of experiencing the odor of a decomposing body. Dead human bodies don't dry up, they melt and the unnatural blend of human chemistry creates vapors so indescribably putrid they can permeate steel. This is no exaggeration. Where bodies have decomposed in automobiles, the odor so permeated the vehicle that it cannot be salvaged for use and must be scrapped. Heat greatly increases the rate of decomposition, so summer is not the time to work on the wagon. Over the years, the wagon men have tried many remedies to overcome or neutralize this putrid odor. Ammonia, a can of fresh coffee strewn about, cigar smoke to mask inhalation; but the only thing that ever worked was a gas mask. On occasion, even some of the hardiest old-time wagon men have retched at the scene. Removing dead bodies is a most unpleasant task, but your policemen do it, their attitude being, "It comes with the job." Anyway, getting back to the recluse, the landlady had a key for his apartment and she let me in. There he was, between the bed and the dresser, lying in a heap on the floor. His bald head had bloated and turned purple and blue. Where the back of his neck couldn't take any more pressure, the tissue had split and the opening was full of maggots. I opened two windows and positioned a fan to expel some of the odor. Advising the squad operator of the D.O.A., I also suggested he tell the wagon men to buy a couple of cigars, they would need 'em. The wagon arrived and here came "Mr. Salty," an old timer with maybe fifteen years on the wagon. "Where're the cigars?" I quipped. With an expression that might lead you to believe he had all the world's wisdom, he answered, "I've handled hundreds of dead bodies; they don't bother me, kid."

Both wagon men then disappeared into the apartment, only to exit, one coughing and Mr. Salty, his eyes full of tears. There are some things you can just never get used to. A decomposing body is one.

We had just arrived at the hospital emergency parking lot, when the other wagon pulled up. Our D.O.A. was a natural death; the other wagon had two bodies from a murder scene. My partner went inside the emergency room, returning shortly with a doctor and nurse. The doctor entered our wagon and uncovered the deceased face. He would ascertain beyond a doubt that the body was in fact dead and pronounce the same. The nurse was jotting down pertinent information, as the other wagon crew jokingly made light of the situation. From our wagon to the other, the doctor would routinely check the bodies. One of the wagon men said, "Look in his mouth, Doc, the bullet might have gone through there." The female victim's blood-soaked blouse was stark testimony to the area of her fatal wound. "No, he was shot through the right temple," the doctor related, as he emerged from the wagon. Our report and the hospital's would now have an official pronouncement and time of death. Policemen intentionally make light of these situations, probably as a defense from getting too emotionally involved. Actual handling of the dead bodies would be involvement enough.

After securing the wagon, we used the hospital washroom to wash up. Time for a coffee break at the hospital lunchroom, where we could sip our coffee and observe the nurses. In a few minutes, we were joined by two sergeants and two patrolmen, one a new recruit. The conversation naturally gravitated towards homicides and dead bodies, subjects not infrequently discussed by policemen. The sergeants seemed to be trying to outdo each other, as they vividly told one incident after the other. "There he was, lying in the alley, back of the garage. He was stabbed fifty times and his chest was torn open, the lungs and other stuff oozing out." The recruit sat there, mouth agape. He was mesmerized by their stories, probably the first ones he had ever heard. One sergeant started to relate a story as though it had happened ten minutes ago, using all the dramatic inflections at his command, and being as vivid as possible. "First the animal raped this young broad," he started. "Then, after beating her to unconsciousness, he proceeded to shove a broom handle about eighteen inches into her vagina. Do you realize how far that is? About up to here," he indicated by putting his hand to the bottom of his rib cage. The recruit winced. "That's not all," the sergeant continued. "Then he jumped on her pelvis, snapping that. Then he broke off the rest of the broom handle that was sticking out, leaving the eighteen inches in her. Remember, that's up to about here," he gestured again. "Now he took the broken part and plunged it into her head." For the finish, the sergeant gestured with both hands, holding the invisible broken broom handle. So vivid and descriptive was his telling of the story, I found myself wincing. And I had heard dozens from other policemen, perhaps not as gory. "And she lived an hour and a half. Can you imagine that?" he said, terminating his story. I had completely forgotten about the body we just delivered. The sergeant's story was one I would have rather not heard. Police work can make a man insensitive to a degree, but if you lose your humanistic equilibrium, you are personally in trouble.

Another beautiful summer day. We sat in the wagon, parked, driver's door open to catch any cooling breeze. My partner was industriously cleaning his gun, intermittently commenting on its condition. Both the

21

police and my transistor radio were going at the same time. Listening to a little music occasionally seemed to take the edge off. It helped you remember everything wasn't revolving around a need for police service, that most people were good and living happy trouble-free lives. Sometimes policemen stereotype society in an unrealistically bad light—a natural reaction even though far from true.

So far the day had been quiet. We had transported an elderly woman who suffered a head injury resulting from two bastards who had snatched her purse. Really kind of a pathetic situation. She was about seventy years old and was returning home from church. Her legs were wrapped with stretch bandages and she probably suffered all the infirmities of old age. Now, here she lay, head bleeding profusely, in a semi-conscious state. Broad daylight and an old woman couldn't even go to church unmolested. Undoubtedly the bastards who did it had a police record and were on probation. Of course, the psychiatrist and pseudo-intellectuals would conclude that the perpetrators were "sick." All this educated brain power wouldn't see this little old lady lying in the dirt, head bleeding like an injured bird. It was comforting to know that those who would escape man's punishment, could never elude the wrath of God.

"D.O.A., 900 W. Clark." The wagon pulled up in front. Peering through the dirty door glass was an elderly gray-haired man. "Did you call the police?" Tony asked. There was no mistaking that it was the right location. The odor let the wagon men know that the D.O.A. wasn't fresh also. Eyes full of tears, the old man answered in a shaken voice, "Yes, my wife is dead." His appearance indicated the old man to be easily seventy or older, bent by the passing years—a face that reflected all the ups and downs that a long life would endure. Motioning to the two wagon men, he led them into his store. Old furniture and the odd assortment of second-hand lamps and appliances were piled helter-skelter all over. Apparently this second-hand store had been in existence many years. It had that musty odor that only time could create. Mixed with the musty smell was the more pungent odor of a body that must have been long dead. It was nighttime and the interior of the store was almost totally dark. One dirty, bare light bulb, suspended by a dust-laden cord, was the only illumination. The old man slowly wended his way through the maze of junk without bumping or stumbling on anything. He could probably do just as well blindfolded. Passing under an old set of discolored curtain stretchers, easily missed by the little old man, Pete muttered, "Son of a bitch," as his six-foot height put his head in alignment with the protruding stretchers. Pete wasn't hurt by the contact, but his hat had almost been knocked from his head. "Don't you have any more light?" he asked, straightening his hat. "I have some candles," the old man answered. Tony chuckled.

Upon reaching the rear of the store, they entered a narrow passageway, apparently connecting the store to a back room. Now, the odor was overpowering. Under their feet, the two wagon men could discern a transition from the filth-laden hardwood floor, to a now soft, spongy surface. Probably rags, they thought. An old chipped ceramic lamp was sitting on a faded oilcloth covered table, its dirty shadeless bulb giving just enough light to see that the back room was as dirty and unkempt as the store itself. The floor of the small backroom was almost completely covered by bunches of tissue, that were discolored by stains. *That* was the spongy softness the officers felt beneath their feet in the passageway. Now the old man was whimpering as he gestured to a darker area of the room. In that area, Pete, straining his eyes, made out a cot. As he walked closer, he could see the dead woman's body, a sheet covering the lower half. After taking one step closer, Pete said, "Oh, God." He turned from the body in haste, his hand to his mouth. He managed to tell his partner, "C'mon Tony, don't even look." Then he made a beeline for the passageway and through the store, stumbling once or twice before he would reach the front door. Outside, he retched. One hand pressed against the side of the wagon, supporting his weight, he bent over emptying his stomach. Moments later, Tony emerged from the store, his face ashen, hand to his mouth. He, too, began to vomit. Both of these men had handled many dead bodies in various stages, but this situation was so stark that even they were overwhelmed. The dead woman had died of breast cancer. Where her breasts had been, were now two cavities, the outer tissues of which bore evidence to the sickening ravages of the cancer. The terrible residues and liquid chemistry of the violated cells was what the tissues on the floor were saturated with. They knew now that this was the spongy mess they had walked on. The devastating sight of a human body eaten away in this terrible manner, and the odor, too foul to describe, was more than anybody's sensibilities could handle.

Pete was first to speak after regaining his composure. "No way I can handle that without a mask." Tony, still visibly shaken, nodded acknowledgment. First advising the police dispatcher, then telling the old man they would need additional equipment, they drove off.

Returning shortly, they donned gas masks and proceeded to complete the grisly task of removing the dead body. In police parlance, this type body is known as a "stinker"—a situation all wagon men dread. So, to all those who think being a policeman is easy . . . I invite them as good citizens to assist the next wagon crew on such a mission.

After leaving the hospital, we resumed patrol. Hour after hour we traversed the beat. The heat of the sun was so intense most would be dissuaded from committing a criminal act . . . just too hot! We hadn't been parked for five minutes when the police dispatcher assigned us to "man having a seizure." As we approached, you could see the usual gathering of gawkers encircling the victim. He was a young man of about twenty-five. Face down, his whole body contorted from what was apparently muscular spasms. We turned him over, placing his head on a blanket. The spasms had diminished and now he began to mumble. Someone in the crowd said, "I know him; his name is Robert Samples and he's pretty drunk." There was a strong odor of alcohol, but, when he didn't respond to the pungent odor from an ammonia vial, we knew he needed professional medical treatment. "Just sit him up, he'll be all right," someone in the crowd said. Usually someone having a seizure responds quite quickly and is coherent, but this man was in some kind of deep trouble, physically. I requested an ambulance, since they could make a better diagnosis and were better equipped. At least they had oxygen, if needed. The victim's face registered the pain he was experiencing, his hand occasionally touching his chest. I opened his shirt to see if he had a chest wound, or a scar, or anything to let us know how to help him. In minutes, the ambulance arrived. A medic took his pulse, then checked his inner arms. Sure enough! He was on hard narcotics. No denying the fresh needle tracks. Alcohol, narcotics and a ninety-degree temperature outside. Who wouldn't go into seizure, or coma? We hurriedly got the victim on a stretcher and away the ambulance went, siren screaming. During the hot summer months, people would be dropping all over the city. Whatever their ailment, the addition of intense heat would overcome their resistance. Even the drunks would succumb to the high temperatures. The wagons would get a workout and so would their sweating crews.

We told the dispatcher the ambulance had taken

the victim and we were now available for assignment. As he acknowledged, we resumed patrol, bouncing down the street, inadvertently finding every pothole in existence.

The Argument

The assignment has been simply, "Woman cut." Such a call could mean she had cut her hand peeling potatoes, or have a much more serious injury. The dispatcher would relay only that which he was told over the phone. Our job was to ascertain the situation and take the necessary action. Apparently the caller didn't think his wife being stabbed in the chest was an emergency. I was first to exit the elevator of the apartment building located in a middle-class section of the district. Down the corridor, standing halfway in the entrance to an apartment, was a husky middle-aged man, wearing an undershirt and slacks. "Better bring a stretcher," he said. My partner, without saying a word, turned around and re-entered the elevator. He was on his way down for the stretcher. "What happened?" I asked the undershirted man. "She stabbed herself," he answered, in a matter-of-fact way. Two things were obvious at this time. His blasé attitude and powerful build. Massive shoulders and a thick chest.

"Who are you?"

"I'm her husband," he answered. No sign of emotional upset or anxiety.

The wife lay on the floor alongside a couch. Not a stitch of clothes on. Blood slowly bubbled from a small cut above her right breast. Suddenly, the bubbles stopped. She lay there, both eyes and mouth wide open. She was dead. Slightly winded, my partner asked, "What is it, Bill?" as he stood the stretcher against the wall. "She's dead," I answered. Joe dropped to his knees alongside the body, checking for any telltale signs of life. "She's gone," he confirmed. The husband just stood there. No reaction at all. "What do I do now?" he queried. I shot Joe a glance, then sarcastically said, "Why don't you sit down and have a cigarette . . . try to relax." He did just that. This guy was unreal. Even I felt some compassion for the dead woman. The bastard even had a smirk on his face. His attitude angered me. "What happened?" I demanded.

"Well, she was in the kitchen doing dishes." Looking towards the kitchenette, I could see a few broken dishes on the floor. I remember thinking, naked . . . she was doing the dishes stark naked? "We had been out earlier this evening for a few cocktails and she thought I was paying too much attention to a friend of hers." As he spoke, I studied his face for some sign of emotion . . . maybe remorse. There was nothing. He just continued on, matter-of-factly. "When we got home, she was still mad and kept arguing. Then she took this knife (walking to the sink, he picked up an old knife, which had been worn thin from years of sharpening and use) and said, 'if I can't have you, Ill kill myself.' I held her wrist and she seemed to relax. And, as soon as I let her go, she stuck herself in the chest." He paused, as though wondering whether we believed him or not. "Then she staggered and fell right where she is now. I didn't know what to do, so I took the knife out, washed it, and then called the police." All the time he spoke, he maintained that unemotional expression. Now finished speaking, his face had that stupid smirk. My anger surfaced again. He had to be lying, no woman ever does the dishes naked. And why wash off the knife? He was trying to make fools of us with this concocted story. I felt a strong dislike for this character.

Even Joe doubted his story. "We better call the dicks, Bill." Joe used the apartment phone. Soon the homicide detectives and the crime lab were at the apartment. They were to hear a completely different version of the incident. In our presence, the husband related that they had been out having a wonderful time, and that she had come from the bedroom and not the kitchen, as we were told. Taking one of the homicide dicks aside, I told him of the gross inconsistencies. "I know," he said. "The bastard's lying; if he doesn't cop out, he's gonna walk." The detective was right. There were no witnesses and it was the husband's word against nobody's. Any case would be circumstantial, and any story he chose to stay with could be accepted as fact.

While the detectives questioned the husband, I searched the apartment for something tangible, that might prove beyond a doubt he had in fact killed his wife. Since he was neat and clean, I looked for blood-stained clothes. The bathroom hamper revealed nothing. Nowhere could I find anything that would be incriminating. In the medicine cabinet, I spotted a folded piece of paper through the clear plastic razor container. In what appeared to be a woman's handwriting, it read ... "I love you, I love you." Maybe she was insanely jealous and did stab herself. But why would he tell two obviously different accounts? Why lie? The dicks had checked out the husband's body. No scratches or marks to indicate a struggle. Even the wife's fingernails were free from the skin of an attacker. All we had at this time was a dubious account, nothing more. A frustrating dilemma. "Listen, I'm warning you right now." Even the detective was angered by the situation. "You're suspect for the murder of your wife." To this, the husband reacted by raising one eyebrow and shrugging his massive shoulders. Out of earshot the detective confided to me, "This guy's the coldest fish I ever saw. We don't have anything, but we'll try anyhow." Their questioning revealed the couple had been married less than six months, after meeting in a bar frequented by gigolos. This particular bar was known for catering to unattached middle-aged women seeking romance. In our victim's case, the romance had lasted less than six months. And for that, she paid the ultimate price. Whether her death was self-inflicted or not was only known by two people—herself and the husky, smirking man that stood before us. One thing for sure, if he had killed his wife, he wasn't telling the police. Not now . . . not ever.

The Idol

"Check on a gas leak."

"10-99," the acknowledgment code for a one-man car. It was about 9:00 P.M. The address was in a black neighborhood. This was before the portable police radios came into being; once out of the car, I was definitely alone. Complainant supposedly lived on the second floor of an old two-story frame. Not a soul in sight, as I approached the front stairs. At the top of the stairs, I paused . . . no odor of gas that I could detect. Someone was behind the door to the entrance. Cautiously, I opened the door, one hand on my revolver. The dim street light partially lit the stairwell, allowing me to see a young black girl, about twenty, standing with her back to the wall. She didn't speak.

"What's wrong?"

"Gas leak," she answered.

"Are you alone?"

"No, my mother and daughter are upstairs."

If there was danger of a gas leak, why would she be out of harm's way, without at least her daughter? Something wasn't right—I could sense it.

"Let's go upstairs . . . what's your name?"

"Darlene," she answered, as she led the way.

The apartment was like hundreds I had been in, ultra-plain, with roaches that scampered around as though they were trying to find a way out. Darlene walked into the living room. Her mother, a heavy-set woman, nodded me over. "Darlene's an outpatient from the mental hospital and she's acting up again." People with mental problems are not what you would suspect. They are quite rational most of the time, no visible signs or unusual manifestations.

Returning with a cigarette, which she nervously lit, Darlene started to explain, "Don't you see, officer? I was making toast," she gestured toward the range, the oven door wide open. Suddenly Darlene said, "Don't move!" her whole manner changing. I froze, the only things moving were the hairs on the back of my neck and my heartbeat . . . which had doubled. Darlene stared at the range transfixed. She slowly reached into her purse. My mind was going two-forty, a knife, straight razor, gun—what was in that purse? By now, my hand was on the grip of my revolver, an instinctive reaction. "Darlene, you cut that out," her mother said. All I could think of was, *why me?* There are two things in police work I don't like to handle—one is drunken women, the other is people with mental problems. Both situations limit a policeman's actions; after all, these are sick people, not felons.

Fortunately, what Darlene sought from her purse was a little transistor radio, which she thrust at arm's length towards the oven. She appeared to squeeze the radio in her hand, saying, "Don't be afraid, I blocked the idol's rays." Looking at me in a more relaxed manner, Darlene asked, "Did you see the idol on the range with the jewel in her forehead?" She had a name for her imaginary idol, which to this day I don't recall. Whatever, there we were.

Her mother coaxed, "C'mon, Darlene, you gonna feel better at the hospital." Darlene looked confused, but was responsive. A small suitcase had already been packed and we started down the stairs. "I'll drive Darlene to the hospital," the mother told me, outside. Instead of following her mother, Darlene went to the passenger side of my squad car, trying to open the door. Her mother, several car lengths ahead, beckoned, "C'mon, Darlene." As her mother approached, Darlene angrily dropped the small suitcase she was carrying. Her face contorted to an expression of pure hatred. "Stay away," she warned her mother. Seeing Darlene's change of mood, I advised Darlene's mother to wait in her car. Darlene cautioned me, "Don't look at her," referring to her mother, "or she gonna have you under her control, too."

"Don't worry, Darlene," I said, "the police department has a truck with lead walls; the rays can't get through that, no way."

"Isn't this a police car?" she asked.

"Yes, but it doesn't have lead walls; lead is too heavy; we have to use a truck."

She was convinced.

The car radio warmed up and I advised the dispatcher of the situation. The truck with the lead walls was on its way. "This is Darlene, guys, make sure the rays can't get at her." The wagon men knowingly assured Darlene she would be safe. She gingerly stepped up and into the squadrol. Her mother followed the wagon to the hospital and signed her daughter in.

Fortunately, gas leaks aren't too common.

Owl Eyes

"Throwing things out the window, between the buildings, second floor rear!" I glanced at my partner, ten
years my senior on the job. "What next?" We knocked
at the door . . . POLICE! The guy that opened the door
looked weird—small, slender, owl-like eyes, made
larger by his eye glasses.

"It's my wife, she's drunk. Look at this." He held
up an empty whiskey bottle that had contained a fifth.

"Where is she?" I asked.

"In the bedroom, this way."

Sure enough, there she was, naked as a jaybird. She
lay there on the bed, glassy-eyed, smiling. "It's the
fuzz: Hi guys."

Eddie turned to her husband. "Get her a robe!"

"Oh," he said, then scampered out the bedroom.

"What's the trouble?" Ed asked her.

"I've been drinking and fucking everybody in long
pants since I found out my husband is queer," she said.
I knew that mope was six points left of center the minute I saw him. "Wanna fuck me?" she asked.

In walked dummy with a see-through nightgown in
his hand.

"Not that!" exclaimed Ed. "Get something
heavier."

Again, dummy said "Oh," and left. This time he
had a heavy cotton robe, which he handed to my part-

34

ner. His expression never seemed to change. It was as though his naked wife was a piece of furniture. Ed helped her into the robe, talking all the time, as you would to an eight-year-old child.

We got her on her feet and guided her into the living room.

"You're big," she told me, as she rubbed a breast against my arm. "I like 'em big."

"Make some coffee," Ed told dummy, who retreated to the kitchen.

"What do you want to do?" I asked Ed.

"Uh, we'll see."

We kept her on her feet, hoping it might help. Her husband brought in a cup of coffee.

"I don't want that," she said. "Let's go for a drink."

"You've had enough," Ed told her.

Her head would slowly drop down, only to be lifted up vigorously. "Queer bastard," she directed towards her husband, who never even winced. *Must be true*, I thought.

She seemed to be gaining her equilibrium, so we released our hold. Ed reached for the cup of coffee. Back she went, half on the coffee table, half on an arm chair. Now the coffee table only had three legs.

"No use, let's get her back in bed, Bill."

We guided her back to the bedroom, easing her on the bed. All the time Ed giving out with the big daddy routine. He tucked her in, till her smiling face was all that could be seen.

"You be a good girl now," Ed told her. I couldn't believe it. I knew this wouldn't work. "She'll sleep it off," Ed told the husband as we left. We retrieved the stuff she had dropped out the bedroom window and left it by their door.

Driving down a side street, we were waved down by a middle-aged man, who related he and his wife had just returned from an anniversary party and she was too drunk to walk. Would we please help her from their car to the apartment. The husband was drunk too, but he knew which end was up. The wife, fairly heavy, was two drinks away from being completely unconscious. At least they lived on the first floor. With no small effort, we got this one in bed.

We hadn't gotten two blocks away when the dispatcher told us to return to the first assignment. This time she was throwing things out the bathroom window, maybe herself! Another two-man car arrived at the same time. We went up together. Owl Eyes, with the same wax expression, advised us that she was in the bathroom and the door was locked. We could hear the sound of falling objects and glass breaking. My imagination went rampant, maybe she took poison, or cut her wrist, or was on the window ledge about to jump. An officer from the other car gave the door a terrific kick. It swung open, the broken lock dangling. There she stood, amidst combs, brushes, towels, wash cloths, and all the sundry things that medicine cabinets contain . . . she didn't have a scratch! All the horizontals in the room held a layer of white powder, probably talcum. Our mischievious perpetrator was also covered with talc. Most of it on the top of her head, shoulders and bare breasts. She was a smiling sight to behold. I extended my hand, which she grasped. Leading her back to the bedroom, I told her, "Let's go for that drink now. Get dressed." She was quite willing, but completely unable to dress herself. Without hesitation, Ed mechanically helped her into her various garments, as though he were dressing his own daughter for school. "Get us a wagon," I quietly told one of the other patrolman. We escorted her down the stairs and into the waiting wagon.

At the women's lock up, she would be safe, but not from the inevitable hangover. Owl Eyes signed the necessary complaints and we were on our way to the station, where arrest forms would be made out. Drunken women can be extremely vicious. This one had a real problem, which she tried to dissolve with alcohol, but she wasn't really bad . . . just desperate. I felt truly sorry for her predicament.

The Sleeper

"Domestic disturbance, 1410 W. May, 3rd rear."

"Ever notice, Joe, they're always on the third. Must be the atmosphere that high, must make 'em screwy."

"Ya know, you're right, Bill; come to think of it, most domestics are on the third . . . or at least the second."

The address was in a relatively nice neighborhood; even this building was in well-kept shape. We climbed the carpeted stairs and were greeted at the top by a middle-aged, nicely dressed woman.

"Please come in," she said. "Would you care for coffee?"

"No, thank you . . . what's your difficulty?"

"Well I'm not really sure I should have called the police, but maybe you can tell me what to do anyway. The last few months my husband has started to act strangely. First, he accused me of having an affair, which of course isn't true. Then, if it isn't that, he's always starting arguments. Sometimes he stays up all night and sleeps during the day. Must be change of life or something."

"Is he home now?" I asked.

"Yes, he's sleeping. Just today he told me I wasn't his wife, and didn't belong here. He said he didn't know me."

"Does he ever get physical?" Joe asked.

"Well, he hasn't, yet . . . What should I do?"

"Where's he sleeping?"

"Right here, the bedroom."

She walked several steps and opened a bedroom door. On the bed lay her husband, a gray-haired, unshaven man about sixty years old. Mouth agape and snoring, he was obviously deep asleep. I closed the bedroom door.

"No point in waking him up now, he's dead asleep."

"Well, can you tell me what to do?" she asked.

"Well, he's peaceful now . . . he's asleep."

Her face assumed a dejected expression. Shaking her head, she said, "You don't understand . . . he can do that."

"Do what?" Joe asked.

"He can be wide awake and just lay down instantly asleep, snoring and everything."

I looked at Joe. Maybe he wasn't the only one going through the change of life. She must be fantasizing or imagining what she told us. Maybe she had a mental problem.

"Well, listen, lady, he's not disturbing anybody now and this isn't really a situation for the police. If he gets physical, call us . . . otherwise you'll have to get a warrant."

Joe nodded in agreement.

"Do you know the procedure in obtaining a warrant?"

"Yes, I know," she said, with an air of defeat.

"If he gets violent though, call us; that's about all we can do now." As soon as I said that, I remember thinking, the old guy's peacefully asleep—if anybody gets violent, it'll probably be her. She must be going through the menopause. Maybe she just wants to dump the old geezer . . . who knows?

On the way down the stairs, Joe said, "Boy, women

39

are really somethin' else; they can really dream up some stories."

"Yea, those hot flashes must be reachin' her . . . poor guy's sure got his hands full."

Joe chuckled, "Yea, and he's too old to put out her fire."

Once in the squad car, I lit up a cigarette and Joe cranked the engine. "Another case solved," Joe quipped, as the car slowly pulled from the curb. For some reason, Joe bent a left at the alley entrance, and passed the rear of the house we had just left. Must have been an act of providence, because as soon as we passed the rear of the building we heard that shrill unnerving scream, and a woman calling for help. Joe slammed the brake on and we both jumped out of the car, clubs in hand. "Help, police!" The shout came from above. We looked up to see our complainant and her husband on the rear porch. She, holding him off at arm's length, and he, menacingly holding up a baseball bat. In less than a minute, we were on the third floor porch. "Where is he?" I breathlessly asked. "In, in the apartment," she answered, gesturing limply. My grip tightened on the club handle as I cautiously entered the rear of the apartment. "Be careful," Joe cautioned.

We checked out each room methodically; one was left . . . the bedroom . . . where he had been sleeping previously. Slowly I opened the door. There on the bed was her husband, mouth agape, snoring in a deep sleep. On the floor alongside the bed lay the baseball bat. "Here he is, Joe." Slipping my club in its holder, I vigorously shook the old man. "Get up! C'mon, get up!" His eyes opened and he slowly raised himself to a sitting position. Looking through glazed eyes in bewilderment, he asked, "What's wrong . . . what happened?" Joe and I looked at each other. The guy wasn't faking it, he had without a doubt just revived from a deep sleep, or comatose state, or twilight zone. Whatever the case, he was just as surprised as we were . . . maybe more. As he tried to stand on the floor, his foot alighted on the baseball bat and his reflexes sat him back on the bed. He leaned forward looking down at the bat. "What the hell is that doing there?" he said angrily.

His wife, standing in the bedroom doorway, obviously much calmer, said, "That's right, he doesn't remember—he never does."

"You mean he won't remember chasing you with a bat?" I asked.

"That's right," she said, as she approached her husband. "C'mon honey, you need help. We're going to help you."

Now standing up rather abruptly, the husband demanded of his wife, "Who the hell are you?" He was completely out of it. The man was definitely mentally ill. "Lousy communists, think they run the world!" He stared straight ahead through glassy eyes, seeing nothing. Then his posture slumped. He slowly sat back on the bed, leaning back all the way. Once on his back, his eyes closed and his mouth opened . . . snoring once again in that deep sleep. For long seconds, no one spoke. The wife's eyes welled with tears. She slowly turned away and left the bedroom. I looked at Joe, his misty eyes shifted down as he fumbled for a cigarette to hide his show of emotion. It was a touching situation and, if you weren't affected by it, you weren't human. Joe and I were reminded of one thing. No matter how strange a related story might sound, in police work it is probably true.

We made arrangements for the husband to be transported to a mental health center where his wife would sign the necessary papers for his treatment. And just before the wagon left, I peered in through the little rear window. Sure enough, there was the sleeper, stretched out on the wagon seat, mouth agape, snoring as soundly as ever . . . to sleep—to sleep . . . perchance to dream.

The Naked Prowler

"Prowler at the door, 146 N. Maple, Apt. 309." In five minutes we were knocking at the door of apartment 309.

A very pretty woman about twenty years old opened the door. She was wearing a thin nightgown, which lightly conformed to the shape of her breasts and nipples. The light from a table lamp filtered through her nightgown, making it known she was wearing panties and had a much better than average figure. "Someone was trying to open my door and I was really frightened," she said. After some comforting words and the assurance we would return in haste to her beckoned call, we left the apartment.

In the corridor, I told my partner I would go down the hallway and check it out. The hallway lighting was fairly dim and as I approached what appeared to be an alcove for refuse and old newspapers, I heard the sound of paper being shuffled. The alcove was dark but my flashlight illuminated the area, wherein to my surprise was a woman about forty-five years old. She stood there completely nude, holding up a sheet of newspaper to hide her nakedness. "I locked myself out of my apartment," she volunteered as she stepped forward, gingerly sidestepping to position herself behind that single sheet of newspaper with the skill of a striptease artist. I must admit, the wicked thought of lighting the sheet of newspaper at the bottom did cross my mind. Words could never do justice to this situation. You have to see her gyrations, while at the same time trying to act blasé. With a straight expression, I asked her the apartment number. When she said 308, we knew the prowler stood before us. Apparently she had gotten confused and tried the door of apartment 309 by mistake. To make the situation a little more bizarre, I found the door of apartment 308 to be open several inches. Our naked lady slowly backed into her apartment and after a soft spoken, "Thank you, Officer," she closed the door. Each apartment had its own bathroom facilities and even if it were a community bathroom, would she go to it naked? For the next hour or so my partner and I tried logically to make the pieces fit. We never succeeded.

Big Mike

"Disturbance in the tavern" . . . This call is always bad news. My partner was a new kid, but attentive and eager to learn. A well-built lad, about one hundred and ninety pounds. Six-one and solidly built. We entered the tavern, where everything appeared to be peaceful. At first I thought we might be at a wrong address. There were several guys at the bar, but no one was louder than a conversational tone.

"Did you call?" I asked the bartender. "Yes, I did," he answered. "See the big fella in the dark suit? Well, he's been on a binge for two weeks since his wife left him and he's talking about cutting someone's head off! You better talk to him; I don't want any trouble in my place." How many times had I heard that before? "I don't want any trouble in my place." Most bartenders will sell you enough liquor to swim in, but as soon as some bastard gets goofy, they're calling the police to throw 'em out. So, while you're home nursing maybe a swollen eye, the tavern owner is adding up the night's receipts. It is tricky, though, to tell a man he's had too much to drink and cut him off. Most people don't even know when they are drunk. The last thing a policeman wants to do is get physical. They get the same paycheck to handle a situation peacefully that they would if they had to do a number on someone's head with their nightstick. Drunks, for all practical purposes are mentally deficient, since alcohol actually anesthetizes the human brain. All react differently and are handled accordingly.

With the aforementioned in mind, I approached "the big fella." And he was big. Maybe six four and two fifty. Massive hands and no gut. As I recall, he was a plumber or did some other physically hard work. No doubt he was in good shape and strong.

"Can we talk to you for a minute?" I asked. Before he could answer, I said, "Let's go sit in a booth; your problem is nobody else's business." Sitting at the bar you could see he was big, but when he stood, his size was even more impressive. Once in the booth, he related how his wife had left him and that he had been drinking day and night for two weeks. "I must be going crazy; now I want to cut somebody's head off," he said. As he spoke, I could see he had consumed so much that he had drunk himself sober. A man in this state can walk and talk quite well, but the dictates of his muddled mind might allow him to do anything. "You need professional help, a doctor. Why don't you go to a hospital?" His eyes narrowed. "I don't want to go to a hospital . . . can't you do something?" *Like a little boy saying he didn't want to eat his oatmeal,* I thought. "Listen pal, if we take you to jail we'll just put you in a cage." I never should have said that. He slowly raised up and, with a great deal of force, brought his tightly fisted hand and forearm crashing down on the table between us. I thought he broke the friggin' table in half! He snarled, "Do I have to kill someone?" Jumping to my feet, I shouted to my partner, who was still seated, "Get out of the booth!" Drawing my nightstick, I stood poised for defensive action. Had our subject attacked us, there is no doubt all three of us would have ended up in the hospital. But he didn't. He just slumped back in his seat. His fury left, like it had arrived, in seconds. Even the snarling face was once more placid. "O.K., let's go!" I told our Jekyll and Hyde. If nothing else, we had to get him out of the tavern. He seemed now to be submissive and sat in the back seat of the squad car not saying a word. As we drove away from the tavern, I wondered what to do next. There is a hospital in our district that had a special unit for alcoholics, but the cost was about two hundred and fifty, cash on the barrelhead. First, we would go into the district station where we could get more muscle, if we needed it.

"What's your name, pal? . . . Well, listen, Mike, we know a place where you can get some help, but its two fifty, cash." Mike said his mother would have the money. I spoke to his mother on the phone and she agreed to meet us at the hospital. This was the third time for me, bringing someone to the alcoholic treatment center.

The corridor of the center had the usual gauntfaced patients. One or two, always pacing back and forth, probably trying to pacify their jangled nerves. Mike, now in a hospital gown, dwarfed the bed he lay on. One of the many nurses gave Mike about an ounce of what I thought to be a sedative. The sedative was in a little plastic container, which resembled a shotglass. Never did find out if that resemblance was intentional.

The room where new patients were brought always had about three or four female nurses. As a matter of fact, the treatment center didn't have any male nurses or orderlies. And, when you did bring someone in, they always asked in a nice way if you wouldn't mind staying 'til the patient was secure. Secure meant that the patient was strapped down to the bed with the use of padded ankle and wrist restraints. On a nearby table was a hypodermic syringe, probably containing some stronger sedative that was fast acting. This I suppose was for patients that were getting physically out of hand, and, since there were no male nurses or orderlies, the little syringe would suffice.

Mike seemed amused by the chattering nurses, as they quickly moved from here to there, tucking him in. All the time chattering, undoubtedly so that he wouldn't become aware they were placing the restraints. One ankle was secure, but, as they tried to draw the leather strap down on his right wrist, he got the message. Abruptly he sat up. "Wait a minute, I might be drunk, but I ain't crazy." His face took on that mean expression. "You behave now," one nurse said. My gut tightened. I could see myself being thrown through the hospital window. Mike could probably "eat" nightsticks. My partner's face turned white. I guess he could see himself flying through the other window. In a low voice, that could undoubtedly frighten a gorilla, Mike said, "Get these fuckin' things off of me." At this stage I was starting to wonder how powerful the solution in that hypodermic syringe was. What if the needle broke? Not a good feeling to know you're going to be severely hurt. Help could never get there in time. Even the nurses looked uneasy. Just then the door opened. In walked a nurse, maybe ten years younger than the others. With a smile on her pretty face, she said, "Hello, Michael, aren't we going to be friends?" He melted. What two 200-pound policemen couldn't do, one little pretty, 110-pound woman did, with a smile and eight words. I'll never forget it. Michael just eased back, a boyish grin on his face.

The nurses had captured Mike and his heart. The restraints were secure and Mike couldn't care less. He was now in the hands of the angels of mercy. "So long, Mike!" In the elevator, on the way down, the new kid said, "If I ever have to go through all that again, I quit!" You could see he meant it. In a tone that I hoped disguised my relief, I said, "Don't worry, you'll get used to it." The rest of the night went smoothly, and towards the end I was glad. Because, before I went home, I would certainly stop for a good stiff drink.

Demi's

Demi's wife was wearing a flowered dress, very summery. She smiled warmly and asked what we were drinking. I always liked Tina, friendly and unassuming, very pretty. At the other end of the bar was Sandra, who must weigh 98 pounds, and her make-up gave her the appearance of a Dresden doll, or something you might win if you knocked down all the milk bottles at a carnival. Sandra was pleasant, though, as were all the people who worked for Demi. Bespectacled, Demi navigated behind the bar, chatting with his customers in their native tongue. Some Polish, Ukranian, or in our case, English. A most congenial man, Demi, rarely in a bad mood. Demi and his wife, Tina, would occasionally smile at each other, and you could see they were perfectly matched.

Demi's is a small neighborhood tavern, whose trade is mostly European. Europeans, generally speaking, are very pro-police, and welcomed the troops when we would stop for a drink after work. I had many good times there over the years. Some nights we would tell jokes, swap war stories, play an occasional game of pool, or enjoy one of Demi's many buffets, celebrating a birthday or holiday event. The first night I ever drank at Demi's, I put a dollar on the bar and three hours later was thoroughly drunk. Not only was my dollar still there, but the addition of a dime. If there was a less expensive place to drink, I sure didn't know where. More alcohol was spilled on the bar than most joints put in your drink. Demi must have bought his stock by the tank car. Not only did he make dynamite drinks, but also bought the house the last one. The juke box ran the gamut from a Polish love song to the screaming rock group types. Demi's was definitely indicative of our district, one extreme to the other, but a good place to drink.

Every night was as different as the customers. One harmless drunk, after consuming enough, would gently kiss a life-sized cardboard bar maid advertisement. On evenings when the pace was slower and you could enjoy a lengthy conversation, I was privileged to hear the true adventures of several European refugees. Their accounts of the invading German troops, concentration camps, and the spellbinding stories of hiding in farmhouses, narrowly escaping capture or death. The emotion-charged words and the anxiety on their faces was ample testimony to the validity of the always fascinating stories. As I would sit there listening, it was easy to forget the street with all its trials and tribulations. Demi's was not just another tavern, it was Americana personified. Many times we stopped there just to see the diverse crowd. On some nights, it was standing room only. The atmosphere was friendly and even a total stranger would feel comfortable. Hours went like minutes and at closing time you wished the gaiety could go on. Even the broads were straight. Most were working girls trying to have a little clean fun and they were never bothered by anyone. The troops made sure of that. Once in a while we brought our wives to Demi's and they never failed to enjoy the evening. Policemen see trouble all through their working hours and, after work, drinking in a place that attracted trouble, was definitely out. The district was full of trouble spots and you could easily find yourself back in the station sign-

ing the papers that would put some trouble-making bastard in the slammer. Or maybe find yourself looking up
from a tavern floor, minus some teeth.

So, for many hours of relaxation and fun, I know I
speak for many when I say, "Thanks, Demi"!

The Liquid Bullet

You didn't have to drink, but most guys did. In some ways the job was very conducive to drinking. For most, it was a social thing and, needless to say, a good percentage of men didn't touch a drop.

After work, some of the troops would stop to have a few, especially if the day had been a hectic one or you were involved in an incident that seethed with excitement and real danger. At the gin mill you could reconstruct earlier situations, criticizing your actions or those of other policemen. During the riots, a few troops often stopped before going home. Some were at different locations during that action, and it was interesting to hear of their involvement. It was also a chance to discuss off-duty social functions. A party, picnic, sports events, or other get-togethers. For a few, the reason was superfluous. An alcoholic quandry was to be their reason. One morning after working the midnight shift, I stopped at Demi's to transact some business. Drinking during daylight hours was never my thing. In appreciation for Demi's cashing my check or whatever, I bought him a drink and ordered a beer for myself. As we sat there making small talk, one of the hard-core drinkers came in. This policeman drank whiskey by the water glass. No ice, no water, no chaser. Just full glasses of whiskey, which he drank down like water. He was only about five years my senior in age, but looked considerably older. I marveled how he could down a water glass of booze in two swallows; one shot would gag me. This particular policeman I had known for sixteen years. Never had I seen him stumble or even sway from the effects of alcohol. Getting louder and his breath were the only signs that betrayed his sober appearance. My beer consumed, I left for home. There was to be a watch party that evening. Would you believe he continued to drink all day, arriving at our watch party about ten o'clock. There he stood, thirteen drinking hours later, still making 'em disappear. The man wasn't even swaying, truly a phenomenon. Six months later he would succumb to the effects of this punishing volume of alcohol. Leaving the hospital thirty pounds lighter, dried out and gaunt faced. He had barely cheated death.

One tour of duty I worked with an admitted alcoholic. His story was like a bad dream, perhaps a nightmare. Drinking to collapse, and reviving to continue. Black-outs and waking up in a panic. Nervously checking his gun to see if any rounds were expended or if his gun was there at all. Stealing change off the bars. The shakes. Unable to write any kind of police report the day after, due to jangled nerves and a befuddled mind. Hating his family life, now in the way of his obsession. Friends and relatives growing more distant. Smashing up his first and only brand new car. Getting sexually involved with women, the types pink elephants saw when they got the D.T.'s. Fighting the hospital bed restraints at several alcoholic wards. Falling into exhaustion from screaming and fighting off the imaginary snakes, bugs, bats, or whatever attacks an alcoholic going through purgatory. His very own delirium tremens. Staring at the ceiling of his hospital room, wondering if he wasn't going crazy. Even as he related his alcoholic odyssey, you could see his anxiety and the perspiration beading on his brow. Admitting his inability to focus on past events with the crystal clarity once at his command. The gnawing fear that he might not be able to stay straight. This he would live with 'til the day he died. For this policeman, one sip of alcohol would be as lethal as a bullet. With the help of God, he would make it. I sincerely hope so. No matter what this man's job was, milkman, garbage man, or priest, he had the innate inability to fend off alcohol. Whatever other reasons made it difficult for him to cope with life, also contributed.

Of the three shifts, the third watch was the drinkers' perfect excuse. Most of the police action happened on the third watch also. The calls for police service at least doubled. Starting at three to eleven or four to twelve, you still had time to subdue that racing adrenaline with a few drinks before going home. For a few, drinking to excess had destroyed their family situation. They had lost their wives, the job, and self-respect. I was lucky. A few drinks once in a while for me was therapeutic. Even the sociability was good. But I knew full well that alcohol is poison and the amount ingested was critical. Also that the swelling of your brain, known as a hangover, wasn't the humorous thing people joked about. More often than not, I had no desire to drink or the time to waste doing it. So, by the grace of God, and even at times drinking more than I should, I never felt endangered by the liquid bullet.

Riots

I was assigned to the Task Force-Beach Patrol the summer of '68. The task force is responsible for maintaining law and order at the city's beaches. This is probably their easiest duty, since they usually are assigned to all high-risk assignments. They are the Marines of any police department, the very best men. The usual calls for service, mostly routine, are given to the beat cars. Task force men respond to all the others, unless assigned to specific details.

They are usually young, lean and very aggressive. When the rioting broke out, we worked four-man cars. One officer assigned to our car, to put it kindly, was an extreme neurotic. He wore a .357 magnum, a .45, a .22 derringer, and had a sharpened wood screw imbedded in the bottom of his night stick for "in fighting." An ice pick to puncture perpetrators' tires, and would you believe a slingshot and a bag of marbles to pelt the taunting hippies. Fortunately these types are very uncommon and dumped when discovered.

We toured the Lincoln Park area, where the hoards of troublemakers were meandering about. There were several thousand unshaven, shabbily dressed, dirty mopes, just spoiling for trouble. They had no cause to champion, just an excuse to flaunt the law—en masse. Vehicles of every description were parked on the grass, in bus stops, or anywhere they would fit.

Some mopes sat on the hoods and roofs of their vehicles. Anticipation of violence filled the air with the electricity of excitement. There would definitely be big trouble. The weather was beautiful and the mopes were sprawled all over the place, some drunk, some appearing to be high on drugs. Some who were innocently conned into thinking it would be a peaceful demonstration, were singing and dancing to the music of tape recorders and portable radios. This gaiety would turn to hatred when darkness cloaked the park. National Guard units started to arrive and I for one was happy to see them. We heard reports that the mob was tearing park benches apart to burn along with tree limbs for bon fires. By now, the mood was escalating towards violence.

Sporadic incidents were igniting everywhere. In Old Town, just west of the park, windows were being smashed. People were running and screaming. There were fights everywhere. Some were bleeding, or limping away. The police loudspeaker blared. "The park is closed, you will be arrested if you remain!" This announcement was answered with a chorus of four-letter words, from the half-crazed crowd which now was over ten thousand. A truck arrived with a battery of searchlights, since most of the park lights had been broken. The searchlights were turned on as about seventy policemen, now wearing gas masks, formed two ranks and marched towards the missile-throwing mob. At another location, a truck bearing a five-foot tank of tear gas spewed out its noxious contents. In minutes the area was laden with a fog-like effect, caused by the tear gas. The wind carried some of the gas eastward to the outer drive where motorists with vision obscured by tears had to stop their vehicles on the spot. Tear gas is extremely irritating to mucous membranes. It makes your eyes tear profusely and burns your sinuses and throat. The worst thing you can do is rub your eyes, and everybody instinctively does just that.

News media personnel were everywhere. After all, they thrive on catastrophe and that's just what this was. There was even a single engine, military observation plane circling overhead. Flash bulbs were popping all over. News media cameramen were taking hundreds of feet of film, and recording the panic-laden sounds. The blue-helmeted policemen and the mob were toe to toe, but the well-disciplined police ranks overwhelmed the disorganized mob. As usual, the news media cameras recorded the policemen repelling physical attacks, but rarely the attack itself. Whether by coincidence or design, or editing of film, the police were made to look like the aggressors. In reality, they were doing their job, enforcing the law, meeting force with legal, overwhelming force. God! they did a magnificent job. Not one shot was fired, or a life lost in this madness. Strategically, it seems in retrospect, that forcing the mob from the park area was wrong. The thinking behind this action was probably that the mob would dissipate, once out of the park—but they didn't! They swarmed into the adjoining streets and went on a rampage of breaking everything in sight. Had they been surrounded by police and National Guard units while in the park, they might have been contained. Be that as it may, since the above is conjecture on my part, now the order was "Clear the streets!" A difficult task, but with additional manpower, it was done with dispatch. Damage was extensive, injuries to both the police and the rioters was light . . . considering the darkness, the thrown missiles and the number of people involved. Even the number arrested was, I thought, shamefully low. This was only one area of rioting; there were more to follow.

I was active at several other disturbances and fortunately not hurt—just ashamed that our society had reached a new low. Shortly thereafter I was at the South Side riots, another disgrace where hatred took the place of reason and understanding. For their valiant superb handling of these riots, the police were to be maligned, criticized, and actually accused of creating some disturbances. This is probably the biggest injustice of all.

Interlude

After taking down all the pertinent information, I walked back to the convertible, handing the driver's license back to the driver. "Just report the accident to your insurance company; they'll advise you accordingly."

She smiled. "Thank you, officer."

As an afterthought, I asked, "Listen, Pam, is there any place in particular that you frequent during your evening hours?"

"No, not really," she answered.

"Well, have a good day. So long."

As I walked back to the squad car, I thought, *Damn! Really a good looker; too bad I couldn't dazzle her with the suave talk, like some guys.* In the squad car, I proceeded to complete the accident investigation report. No big thing. What's known as a fender bender. Pam and her girl friend had slightly dented the fender of another car. Damn! If they weren't both good lookers. Putting it out of my mind, I became engrossed in the report. A passing car sounded its horn. I looked up to see Pam and her girl friend drive by waving. After a few minutes, they passed again, this time pulling to the curb in front of the squad.

"Can I help you?" I asked.

She smiled and said in a friendly little girl manner, "You never did tell us your name, officer. Well, Bill, if you would like to see us later, my girlfriend will bring her boyfriend along and the four of us can meet somewhere."

I knew just the spot.

After telling Pam the time and place, she drove off. "Bye, Bill, see you later."

After work, I drove directly to the Zodiak, our rendezvous. We arrived simultaneously. The Zodiak was fairly nice. It had the usual type bar, but the booth and table seating arrangements were very plush. The four of us just relaxed, having a light conversation. Pam's girlfriend, Margaret and her boyfriend, Bob, were both friendly and interesting. Pam was not only attractive, but intelligent. I watched her every move. She was exceedingly graceful, at times resembling a model.

As the evening progressed, it became more obvious that Pam was not just another shallow broad. Indeed, she was sensitive, charming, and very warm. Bob and I went to the bar for drinks.

Bob, why don't you drive Pam and me to get her car. We'll say we're going to meet somewhere. You take Margaret and I'll split with Pam."

Bob liked the idea. "Sounds good, let's go."

Once behind the wheel of Pam's car, we headed for the lakefront. It was warm outside and the lakefront would be cool . . . secluded. Pam didn't seem to mind that we wouldn't meet Marge and Bob. She agreed that they probably wanted to be alone anyway. We found ourselves to be quite comfortable together. No pretense or fabricated conversation, but an effortless, friendly understanding. Even a need for each other's warmth. In time, we would satisfy that need. The blend was exciting, but gentle, almost spiritual. It wasn't just physical sex. Touching her hand was moving, like a light kiss. She could arouse me with her eyes; even her voice had a sexy softness.

Lighting up a cigarette, I sat back and in my mind

composed the words I would speak. "I am sorry, Pam, taking advantage of you the way I have." Pausing between sentences, I was dead serious, and wanted her to know it. "I really do like you, Pam. Just to be in your company, to be with you." She knew I meant it.

Leaning closer and looking deeply into my eyes, she said, "I like you, too, Bill."

We had been parked for several hours and now the sky was getting light. "Why don't we go to my apartment and I'll make breakfast."

"You sure you want to bother, Pam?"

"Yes, Bill, I do."

As she walked up the stairs in front of me, I watched her shapely legs and the sway of her hips. Her body was artistic from any angle.

The apartment was neat and clean as a pin, even the clear glass ashtrays sparkled. She busied herself, preparing to make breakfast. My uniform was wrinkled and I could sure use a bracing shower.

"Pam, would you mind if I took a shower?"

"No, Bill, go ahead. Leave your uniform on the door and I'll iron it."

"That won't really be necessary, Pam."

"Don't be silly; I want to."

The shower felt good, stimulating. As I briskly dried myself, there was a knock at the bathroom door.

"Here, Bill, put these on; you'll be more comfortable." She handed me a pair of men's pajamas.

For all the time I had known Pam, our relationship was like a very pleasant dream. Whoever heard of a woman that never had headaches, backaches, or ever argued. Looking better in the early light of dawn than most after eight hours at a beauty parlor. Making love with Pam was a symphony of deep feeling and tenderness. She dressed like a model and undressed just as tastefully. Always surrounded with the aura of flowers and perfume. Beautiful white teeth and a sensuous look that never failed to arouse my manhood. In many ways letting me know that she existed just to please me. Once when I asked why, since she could probably have any man she wanted, she answered, "Because I like you." For her it was that uncomplicated. For myself, it was overwhelming. I loved her deeply. She was just about the most unselfish person I had ever known . . .

After slipping into the pajamas, I entered the small kitchenette. On an ironing board lay my trousers. The shirt neatly ironed and hanging from a chair back.

"I've eaten, Bill. You have your breakfast while I shower."

Would you believe, I thought at the beginning we were really just going to have breakfast. Even as I sat there eating, the sound of the shower in the background tempted my imagination, but even then I wasn't sure. She appeared, her lithe body graced by a filmy, smoke-colored nightgown. Through the gown you could see her breasts and the black lace panties. Now I was sure.

"How was your breakfast, Bill?"

"Fine, even the coffee was good."

The words might have come from a tape recorder. My whole being was captured by her natural beauty. She approached me and just stood there. Neither of us spoke a word. I gently kissed her on the neck, cheek, and lightly on her soft mouth. My hands were at my sides as though the vision might disappear were I to touch it. Slowly she placed her warm hand in mine. Qur hands now clasped, she turned, leading me to follow. For countless, precious moments, we were to-know ecstasy few could imagine. Both of us giving without reservation, without shame. Fate had been kind, but destiny would have its way. In time we were to part. After all, the days and nights, it was over.

As time went by and the seasons changed, I knew we could never really be separated. The joy we had shared together, caressed by the warmth of love, would be in our memories when all else had turned to dust.

Were I to find a love so dear, that it might end . . . my greatest fear.

Fallen Angels

Sitting there in the restaurant, just going from one subject to another, somehow we got to discussing the
women that worked in go-go joints, strippers, and finally prostitutes. "There's really a good book there," I
remember saying. To be sure, that whole spectrum is
fascinating. In time I would devote the effort to writing
a book on this subject. Every facet: the pimps, the dan-
cers, strippers and the fallen angels. What these women
could relate would be hard to comprehend. One such
woman who plyed her trade in our district, now dead
from an overdose, was quite frank in telling of the odd
situations she herself had taken part in. Money alone
was not the paramount reason these women had gotten
involved; the reasons were many. For most, the excitement of perhaps getting caught, even being caught,
would in some way elate their psyches.

For the strippers, gossamer garments floating and
swirling as they deftly strut and pirouette on the
hardwood floor. For them, the knowledge that their
every move was followed by hungry male eyes. Being
the coquette was part of their psyches. Revenge on men
would fill a gap for some. Of course, exhibitionism and
other personality quirks would play a part, but the tease
was the real reason, whether they would admit it or
not. Certainly a good many were extremely attractive
and could easily marry a man monetarily successful.

Money was only secondary. The prostitute was much more psychologically involved. For her, a risk of danger, even death, was always present.

The men who seek the services of the streetwalker are from every walk of life. Most are married men from average social levels. While their family is home sleeping, they would be on the prowl for loveless sex.

Pulling to the curb where the whore would saunter over to negotiate price. That arrived at, our suburbanite would slowly drive around the corner. His passenger door open, the whore would simply hop in. She would direct him to a location somewhere remote. After paying the agreed upon amount, some loveless sex act would commence. The whore's body probably containing semen from her last trick, or worse, some form of venereal disease. For this, the sucker would pay. And, if he was really unlucky, a couple of skulking figures might emerge from the shadows and, after taking all his money, leave him a bloody mess. To the police, he would conjure up a tale of being robbed on the street when, out of the goodness of his heart, he stopped to offer a nondescript hitchhiker a ride. This he would do to account for his condition and lost money. His wife sympathetically shaking her head would probably say, "And where are the police when these things happen?" Some suckers, trying forcibly to get more than they paid for, learn the hard way that many whores carry the jagged neck of a broken bottle, straight razors, knives, razor blades, ice picks, or any other weapon that could reduce a two-hundred-pound man to a bleeding helpless mess in seconds.

The prostitutes, usually in control, don't always have the last laugh either. That soft-spoken trick that she had directed to the most secluded place she knew may turn into a Jack the Ripper. A woman hater. Quite often bludgeoned, mutilated female bodies are found in motel rooms, or some back alley, partially covered by garbage. Their faces a death mask of horror. With society's tongue-in-cheek attitude about prostitution, little notice would be given. Even the attempt for someone to identify or claim the body, now at the morgue, might be fruitless. Space in most newspapers would be filled with more important things, like a baseball score or something else that the public would rather be made aware of. Most people didn't really care. If the victim belonged to a stable, the pimp's word for girls under his control, he would simply find a replacement. His conscience free from guilt, with the twisted reasoning that his girls weren't forced, but rather "anxiously" solicited his services.

The relationship between the girls and the pimp differed with each girl. Using every guile at his disposal, he would control their lives diabolically. First, he was crudely masculine, something every woman would respond to. In some ways, a father image. Last, but not least, ironically enough, their sexual lover. For all the girls . . . a mentor. Not the dictionary definition as "A wise, loyal advisor," but rather a sly, clever, unscrupulous bastard, that fed off the weaknesses of the much less intelligent girls. To insure the highest rate of income, he would play one against the other. All would work the street endlessly vying to be the pimp's number one "woman." The number one fool might be lavishly treated with more of the pimp's sexual attention, or perhaps a piece of jewelry and some article of clothing. This she would flaunt at the faces of the other girls in the stable, as a badge of achievement. The fact that her money paid for it was irrelevant.

Aside from the competitive aspect, the pimp would find every girl's weakness or insatiable need. By different degrees, he would satisfy all. A girl smarter than the rest, or one he suspected losing control over, he would hook with narcotics. His web designed to contain all, would be woven with Satan's help. Should a girl get arrested or become sick, he would be there immediately. Paying her bond or medical expenses would be interpreted by the stable as *care*. To the pimp, it was simply a necessary investment towards good business. The sooner a bond was paid, the sooner a girl would be back on the street. Books were never kept, the money was dutifully given to the pimp. To hold out was an invitation for a beating. He would dole out enough for the girl to eat and pay rent for some sleazy apartment. His lifestyle would be an extreme contrast. Nothing but the best. A Cadillac car, velvet cardigan and an apartment furnished to guarantee all the comforts of life. When a girl became chronically sick, physically unattractive or for any reason unproductive, she would be abandoned. The junkies would be overdosed. Most wouldn't live past thirty-five and if they did they would look like sixty. The stable would change constantly, but the pimp would remain . . . the biggest whore of all.

The elite of the hookers is the call girl. Her pimp would be the telephone. These women, oftentimes well-educated and always extremely attractive, work free-lance. The best things in life always cost more, and they were no exception. Their favors sometimes commanding prices well over a hundred dollars or as much as a client was able to pay. These women have fewer psychological hangups than their street-walking sisters. Money and what it buys is their incentive. Living in plush apartments, wearing the best clothes, harboring the false notion they are independent of men, now their sole benefactors. And I suspect these benefactors come from every walk of life . . . bar none. The confidentiality and anonymity would allow any man to have illicit sex with almost no chance of disclosure. For, whether he wore a crown on his head or grease on his hands, nature had embodied in every man a tremendously strong sexual drive. Wives never seem to understand the enormity of that drive . . . the hookers do. They skill-fully had learned how to mother a man or fulfill his fantasies. The low income working man's counterpart would, like everything else have the best . . . even the best whores. Recommendation of their ability was the call girl's best advertising. Their phone usually ringing constantly. Working where and when they wanted, vacationing in exotic places and having the best of tangible things. About the only thing the "easy money" couldn't buy would be the loss of their self-respect.

The police department has a unit responsible for arresting "specifically" call girls. But most are ex-tremely clever and can spot a cop two blocks away. One call girl whose vision must have been blurred this particular night, was arrested by vice detectives. I was working the wagon that night and we were assigned to assist the detectives at a given location. It was a mod-ern apartment building and once inside the plush apartment the dicks introduced themselves, then di-rected us to transport the arrestee to the women's lock-up. She stood before us looking like the cover of a woman's fashion magazine. A wide-brimmed black hat, teasingly canted to one side, a black and white herringbone weave, two-piece outfit, and black patent leather high-heeled shoes. Were I a modeling agent, I would have signed her on the spot. She was magnifi-cent. Her face had all the classic planes of a model, set off by orchid blue eyes. "You're arresting her?" The de-tective nodded his response. Talk about strength of character, this man certainly had it. All the way from the apartment to the women's lockup, her beautifully shaped mouth never uttered a word. Undoubtedly she was angry with herself for being duped by the detec-tives. Next time she would be more careful. But re-member before you condemn, you who cheat on your income tax for far lesser amounts, remember that in the long run these women pay a price so dear, it's immeasurable. Can you imagine what they must think of themselves when alone? Behind that painted facade, the profane mouth and the false bravado, was a little girl that had gotten lost. No matter how coarse they may have gotten, I'm sure they must often cry in lonely desperation. They are used, but never really wanted. Totally alone. No true affection, tenderness or other human being that cared if they lived or died. For, in reality, they too are victims . . . our 20th-century Magdalenes.

District Station

District stations varied in some ways. At one, located in a better section of the city, you could eat off of the highly polished floor. At another in the so-called "fast" district, you could actually make an "on view" arrest. Since just about any given weekend, they were filled with the obnoxious: drunks, both men and women, and the sniffing, twitching, marijuana-stained-fingered, slurred-speaking junkies. "Say man, I know my rights, man. You pigs is harrasin' us good citizens, man." Then, there was the much less than normal types, sometimes lying prostrate on the station floor, others sitting crosslegged, meditating or worshipping some figment of their imagination. Of course, the usual dirty, lost kids, sitting behind the desk, eyes wide open, probably wondering if all adults were this screwed up.

On one occasion, there was a girl sitting behind the long counter known as the sergeant's desk. I guess she was about nineteen or twenty. She was being detained for some reason or other. Perhaps awaiting transfer to the women's lockup. But, without any obvious provocation, she slowly lifted her tee shirt, exposing her braless, beautifully shaped breasts. Picking up one of the many cancellation type stamps, she proceeded to stamp her breasts. God only knows what the hell that was all about.

At times some combatants would continue their

hatred in the station, swearing at each other, and finally locking in mortal combat, only to be separated by the desk officers. Most of these mixed up souls were under the influence of alcohol or some other drug.

New stations had replaced the really old buildings where their unfinished floors had actually been grooved from foot traffic. I had been in the old district stations with their wooden lockers and old pictures on the walls. Most pictures were groups of policemen long since dead, wearing handle bar mustaches and sporting the old so called pie plate stars. When the rusted locks had been removed from the never-used wooden lockers, the dust laden interiors surrendered some old police forms and leather accessories that crumbled to powder upon touch. To the best of my knowledge, none of these stations were saved from the bulldozer, truly a gigantic loss.

Doubtlessly these facilities handled much the same problems as the newer district stations. Unfortunately, people are very slow to learn that they themselves created the predicaments that now smothered them. Every station has its own lockup which, regrettably is never empty. The most frequent guest is the drunk. Some are so stuporous that even after being contained in a steel cell, approximately six by eight, they continued their tirades of swearing, hollering, singing, or kicking some part of the cell, until exhaustion forced them into blissful sleep. For obvious reasons, men and women have separate lockups at different locations. The women's lockup contained everything from arrest for disorderly conduct to prostitution cases. Bringing women prisoners to the women's lockup, for me, was always distasteful. I don't like to see women caged. To see and hear women at their worst completely turns me off. Don't misunderstand me, I have taken part in arresting one tiger that took three other six-foot policemen. One for each arm and leg. This was done so that she wouldn't be hurt, but I'm sure she would have tried to castrate any one of us with a well aimed kick. And many are the policemen that have been bitten and severely hurt by the fairer sex. Without question, I would rather take on a two-hundred pound man than one, scratching, biting, wiry hellcat. So, in addition to keeping women confined preceding court, some were confined so that they couldn't hurt themselves or others. Even though it was necessary, I still didn't like to see it. Whether a Sunday afternoon or five o'clock on any weekday morning, the district station always had some kind of activity going. On the desk in the back room would sit the proceeds from a burglary, or perhaps a gun and cartridges used in a stickup. The scowling prisoner sitting there handcuffed, begrudgingly giving the information required for the various forms.

A never ending drama, while most of the city's citizenry slept . . . peacefully unaware that crime has no timetable. From the fallen drunks to the fallen angels, the beat patrolman would handle all. Most would be guests of the . . . district station.

The Troops

As I've stated earlier in the book, policemen are like snowflakes—no two alike. Some have college degrees and some never finished high school. Some are profound and some slightly profane. They are taxpayers, fathers, most races and colors, fat, skinny, tall, short, young and old. Just one segment of society. They, like any other group, have idiosyncrasies. But, by virtue of their job, they best relate to each other. It's true that their job is most unique. An outsider, no matter how great his or her imagination, could never really comprehend the lifestyle of a policeman. It's not just a job, it's a way of life. Even though policemen have a tremendously strong bond, they are still individuals. Different points of view, many different likes and dislikes. Other than being policemen, they are like most other people. However, I'm sure you will agree that, if you could pick all the people to live on your block, policemen would probably be one of the best choices. Being in a car with a man for eight hours a day enables you to get to know him quite well. Probably better than your own brother. Every man has an intellectual profile of his very own. Each profile is at a different level, based on life experiences that create the sum total. Of course, the level of idiosyncrasies varies also. Here are just a few. One donkey that is constantly late for roll call. I think you know who that is. And, if that's not bad enough, he's also got a reputation for not buying drinks.

Another lad who had a skin problem with his feet was advised by his doctor to aerate them. I would like to deny that he drilled holes in his police shoes, but I can't. In his defense, I will have to admit he didn't have them on at the time.

There was a place in the district where you could get a chicken meal free, and that had to be the best price. I thought my partner would be pleased to hear that, but he insisted on going to an Italian restaurant. A beef sandwich or pizza might not be a bad idea, anyhow. What do you think he ordered? Chicken! And paid the full price. I must be slow because I completely missed the wisdom there.

One guy bought his hot dog at one location and his french fries at another. What a savings he was making. Probably saved enough to have his mop bucket soldered when age rusted a hole in it.

If the man who told me the following story hadn't kept a straight face while telling it, I might not believe it. It seems for some reason or other, he couldn't have sex. But he studiously revealed what he used as a clever substutite. "This I'd really like to know," I remember saying. "Poetry. . ." he said. Poetry! He actually said he wrote poems to take the place of sex. Come to think of it, my wife might like me to write a poem, on one of those nights when she has that splitting headache. The police department's poet laureate had more words of wisdom to offer. "Ya know most policemen don't handle themselves well enough on this job. The name of the game is keep your cool." "That's true," I interjected. "Yea, lose your cool—play the fool. Ya got to analyze the situation, then make your play." I sat there wondering how he had developed such an adamant point of view after only eighteen months on the job. Before he could speak another word, the radio assigned us to investigate "Man at the door." The dispatcher didn't elaborate. Not a life-or-death situation or any immediate peril. Perhaps a drunk or someone simply on the wrong floor of the apartment building. Even the location was close. The poet snapped to a rigid sitting position of attention. Gas pedal halfway to the floor, he shifted to drive using such force that the shift knob flew off. Rear tires squealing, the squad car vaulted forward with such abruptness, I was prevented from leaning forward to retrieve the shift knob. The car fishtailed down the street, mars light and siren clearing the way. In two unnerving minutes, we screeched to a halt at our destination. The poet walked towards the entrance in what could be best described as a subdued run. After pushing the elevator button vigorously, he started to pace back and forth like a nervous, caged animal. "I can't wait," he said. "You take the elevator; I'll take the stairs." With that, he catapulted up the stairs two, three, at a time. I shook my head in disbelief. Almost immediately, the elevator door opened, as though it were waiting for the poet to leave before doing so. I stepped in and pressed the button by number three. On the third floor, the elevator door opened. Here came the poet, Mister Cool, charging up the stairs. He stopped at the third-floor landing, too out of breath to speak. In his spent condition, he could have been pushed over by an eight-year-old child. If there was any trouble now, he would be useless.

Knocking at the apartment door in question, I could hear the poet behind me gasping for air, as though someone punched him in the stomach before each breath. An old woman answered the door. "No, no trouble that I know of," she said. "Maybe it was a drunk on the wrong floor," she suggested. As we stepped out of the elevator on the main floor, it was obvious that the poet's breathing was still less than normal. "Better let me drive 'til you get your breath." He sheepishly nodded in agreement. Undoubtedly he had analyzed the panic of his behavior and realized that when you lose your cool—you play the fool.

Once, on the midnights, I worked with a new policeman who drove quite fast. He drove onto a main street and accelerated up to seventy-five miles an hour. And we weren't going anyplace! So, in a calm manner, I asked him if there was any particular reason he was driving seventy-five miles an hour. "When else can you drive this fast on Grand Avenue?" was his inane answer.

Here are some rather interesting one-liners said by policemen:

If this park could talk.

That car's as hot as a doornail.

What does a guy care after he's dead?

Do gorillas eat soup?

Am I drunk?

I'll never forget what's his name.

The neighborhood was in transmission.

This last story isn't really funny, but true. Over a cup of coffee, one policeman confided that he worked part time, doing some kind of metal fabricating for a large retail chain store. He boasted making fifty thousand dollars gross. "Why work on the police department when you can work full time for the chain store and make a hundred thousand dollars a year?" I asked. "What for? What would I do with all that extra money?" he answered. I know you thought policemen were perfect—sorry to burst your bubble.

The foregoing was on a lighter note, just a little humorous facet of policemen. However, the dimensions are not always light and humorous. Indeed, most times they are deadly serious. Every day a policeman reports for work, he is fully aware he stands on the threshold of death's door, wondering if fate will bid him enter.

No one even bothers to let the public know that hundreds of policemen are killed every year. Not dozens but hundreds. Across our land these fine men have given their lives to protect yours. Thousands are injured doing just the same. These men had families, mortgages, and probably many of the same problems you do. Some were in their early twenties, the flower of their youth. They were doing a job most elements of society are eager to criticize but wouldn't do themselves. Most of the time police work is completely thankless. Being a cop is to be on a tightrope. Not much margin for error. A reaction either too fast or too slow could put you in prison . . . or the cemetery.

The simple so-called domestic could be a policeman's doomsday. Many have thrown a seven during a high-speed chase. A decision that a cop sometimes must make in seconds is analyzed for hours by those who undoubtedly never were faced by a similar situation. And the loudest critics usually have no idea of what police work and its problems are. Everybody wants traffic enforcement . . . for the other guy! Some policemen have been killed simply because they wore a police uniform! I'm not saying policemen are without faults, but who could cast the first stone? At least they try to keep organized society organized. It ain't easy. Many times the blue is stained by red in the effort. For every policeman who has fallen, there will be thousands more to pick up the banner.

Command on the police department isn't just a lonely position; it's the ultimate challenge. To satisfy the administration, the troops and the public is no small task. Yielding to pressures from the powers that be, most men in supervisory positions are forced to sharpen the blade of temperance. The credo handed down from above is that "nice guys finish last." Smothered by bureaucratic edicts and totally impractical demands, most supervisors have the moral strength of character to still be "good bosses." Above all else, first you were a man, secondly a policeman.

At every level of command, there are splendid examples of leadership. Knowing full well that taking a tenacious stance of righteousness would cripple their chances for advancement, they would still spit in the face of bureaucracy to "do the right thing."

The latest technique used to insure ultra-obedient control was the playing of one level of command against the other. This manipulation would deter and prevent some men at supervisory levels from making command decisions. Fearing criticism from the hierarchy, transfer and/or reduction of rank, some bosses might not back up the troops when the chips were down. The most submissive were now the most secure . . . and first to be advanced. Naturally this atmosphere would affect all, and, as it filtered down through the ranks, its most detrimental end result would be thrust upon the patrolman . . . by far the most defenseless. Realizing their precarious position, many good policemen would resign in frustration, aware that being overly aggressive simply put you further out on the limb. Most policemen would swallow their pride and turn the other cheek. They would shrug off the weight of bureaucratic oppression and gain even more strength of determination as they contrasted themselves against all the brown-nosed yes men.

The public is not just a statistic, it's men, women and children—it's people! They need protection and help. They demand it; they deserve it; and despite the ivory tower crowd they would get it! We can't afford to be so efficient that our purpose suffers. So, rest assured, from the highest level of command to the street patrolman, even though limbs are bending all over the place . . . the job will be done.

Black and White

With society pushing for integration, the police department had to be one of the better examples. The department was always integrated, but to a lesser degree. Only a fool would say whites could do a better job in a black neighborhood, or vice versa. This is true of whites or blacks, in a Spanish neighborhood or any area where a culture difference was great. From time to time black and white officers worked beat cars together. Probably for no other reason than to show that the police department was integrated. The practical aspect of this arrangement is completely without logical foundation! Blacks relate to each other in ways a white could never comprehend. By the same token, whites probably did the same. Words alone, not their definition, but their inference, meant different things to different people! Even their physical stance, now known as body language, was different. To know what the difference meant, you must know the origin. A given expression or gesture are all forms of communication. Just the use of words is woefully inadequate. Knowledge of a lifestyle and its varied differences to your own, are extremely important in communicating. Certainly the black police officer is more capable of working among his own people. He knows and understands their needs. He also knows what they're "saying" even when they don't speak! In other levels of communication, like buying a suit or a bag of potatoes, the understanding is simple and unemotional. In police work most citizens involved are highly emotional and most times the situations have potential danger. Not being able to comprehend the facts reasonably fast can be costly.

The black officers I have worked with were very capable men. They knew the streets and alleys of the black neighborhoods. Who was and who wasn't, and where to find who was. During the tours of duty I worked the beat car with a black officer, I was content to observe his techniques and demeanor; usually letting him handle situations where blacks were involved. They were pure magic. We would leave the scene of a disturbance where previously angry people were now smiling and friendly.

Communication was definitely their asset and they used it. The average black officer, by virtue of his job, sees the problems between blacks and whites in a much better light. Never have I seen one of these officers cross the color line in doing their job. They were fair and impartial and most professional. You were right or wrong—not black or white.

Yellow Paper

Who does a policeman call when he's in trouble? In the department, when you make a mistake the answer is—put it on yellow paper. This is called a "From—To." From: patrolman blah blah—To: Commander blah blah. Yellow paper. Whether you just caved in the front of a brand new squad car or were late for roll call by two minutes. Myself, being fairly imperfect, I figure conservatively, to have made out about one thousand such reports. Their destination was determined by your transgression. From the cost of your ink to write it, to a pink slip, if you couldn't justify your actions.

The department was more than fair in most cases, but, if you went to church drunk and shot the stained-glass windows out, words might be a little hard to come by in composing your "From—To." Some men have been caught by inspectors, not only off their beat, but out of their district. For a few compositions covering such a transgression, the Pulitzer Prize could have been awarded. But, since we are judged by our deeds and not our words, a suspension was awarded instead. To err is human, to forgive divine. Sometimes I thought only the patrolmen were aware of that bit of wisdom. It always did strike me funny, though, to see some donkey like myself sitting there with ballpoint poised, searching his vocabulary for the magic words that would make it all go away. I'm sure the bosses had some pretty good laughs in their office, only to return with a stern expression and say, "Don't let that happen again!"

When you did something really serious, an investigation would be initiated. The findings, based on the facts, would determine your punishment. You could refuse to accept the punishment and go before the board, but you had better be right and be able to prove it. Something in the area of a felony, either by involvement or association was beyond any redemption. Most of the "From—To's" were for very minor infractions and, if all were stacked, we wouldn't need a rocket to get to the moon. We could merely walk there on "From—To's!"

I have dented a few squad cars and made a few moves that weren't too clever, but being late for roll call was my biggest hang-up. Twice I had been suspended for that very same reason. But once, when I worked for a different police agency, I was late and missed my elevated train. That particular train crashed, severely injuring many people. Had I been on time, my name may have been on the list of injured.

Come to think of it, were I to relate this story in the narrative of a "From—To," it might sound fairly acceptable . . . the next time I was late for roll call.

The Good Guys

Everybody knows that the good guys wear white hats. In the police department, the traffic division men wear white hats. I worked in the traffic division for several years on an accident investigation car, downtown intersectional traffic control, and motorcycle parking enforcement. Some of the police department's better men are in the traffic division, since they work alone and are solely responsible for investigations and reports of accidents—in an area seventy-five times larger than an average district beat. If you arrived at the scene of an accident on the expressway, where cars were strewn all over the place, you had to know the most expedient way to care for the injured, clear the wrecks, get the traffic flowing, make the reports and, at the same time, stay calm. Try this in a blinding snowstorm. Sometimes pacifying irate motorists blaming each other for the accident requires an ability most traffic men were skilled at. As a traffic man, you see victims of accidents severely injured, bloody faces, broken bones, tongues bitten in half, and young children either screaming or whimpering "Mama." The latter has many times brought me to tears.

The traffic division also had its exciting moments. One incident I recall vividly, probably because I was shiny new on the job, was when, during routine patrol on an expressway, a car ahead of me was weaving from one lane to the other. *The driver must be drunk,* I thought, as I switched on the Mars light and accelerated closer to the suspect car. Instead of pulling over like the previous traffic violators did, the car shot forward. My gut tightened; it would be a chase. No way to know why the driver was eluding the stop. Maybe he had just left the scene of a crime. The police car was one of the specialized expressway pursuit types. Unless the perpetrator could go faster than 120 miles an hour, he would be mine. Damn if he wasn't trying . . . we were both doing 90 plus. He got off the expressway and swung back on, going the opposite way. The son of a bitch wasn't going to be easy. "Stay calm, don't shout into the mike, give us your location and direction of travel." Stay calm! At 100 miles an hour, the siren going full blast, one hand on the mike, the other a death grip on the steering wheel. I was gaining, but only because the suspect car had reached its maximum speed. Suddenly the pursued car veered to the right towards an exit ramp. Sliding sideways, the car went over the low curb and onto the grass, plowing over two young trees, finally flipping over and landing back on its wheels. Wow! Just what I needed—I was really as taut as a bowstring now. Pumping my brakes, I slowed down enough to turn around. As I approached the vehicle, a youth jumped out and was beckoning to someone else in the car. The fool wanted to continue on foot, but his passenger, a 15-year-old girl, was so shaken she couldn't even move. Had the driver run, I might have shot him. This was my first chase and I must admit I was a bundle of nerves. Now you could see blue Mars lights coming from every direction, a most welcomed sight. By the grace of God—the kids didn't even have a scratch. The car had flipped so fast, they never left their seats. It turned out that the kid driving had stolen this car and eight previously. The girl was totally innocent, thinking it was his auto. In court the kid got a year's probation. After all, he was only 16! And policemen get paid to take risks, don't they?

Directing traffic in any large city is no small effort. During the rush hours the hordes of pedestrian traffic are like wandering sheep. They seem to have no regard for their own safety, disobeying traffic lights and any other device designed to protect them. Between tending the flock, answering limitless questions like, "Where am I?" and sidestepping cars, you find yourself literally dancing in the intersection. Once, when nature called, I left the intersection for five minutes, returning to find traffic backed up for several blocks in every direction and people squeezing between the cars at the crosswalks. A most important function, the intersection traffic man.

Another important area is traffic enforcement. When you are stopped by a traffic policeman for some violation, be prepared to receive a ticket. Some people have said a traffic man would write his own mother a ticket. Let's just say they are very conscientious about enforcing traffic laws. This attitude is probably the result of seeing hundreds of people hurt in accidents. Before the advent of the meter maids, the traffic division used three-wheel motorcycles to enforce meter and other parking violations. These ruddy-complexioned hardy men, out in below-zero weather, were said to have the fastest pens in the police department. They could write a ticket and be out of sight before the ink dried. Thus they avoided a lot of sob stories, like "Officer, I only stopped for two minutes, to have the battery in my pacemaker replaced." The public never really embraced these men, but, after all, they are just doing their job.

Always remember! The good guys wear white hats.

Odds and Ends

Then there was the burglary where nothing was taken but the burglar left "his" shoes.

The guy who came into the station demanding to be arrested because he was drunk and drove to the station in that condition. He insisted on being arrested for drunk driving.

The drunk who drove up the upper ramp of a car carrier, thinking it was a bridge.

The arsonist who accidently set "himself" on fire.

The old woman who "saw" invisible men in her yard.

One guy drank a can of lighter fluid because he wanted to see what it tasted like.

I responded to a disturbance call in a snack shop and upon entering I noticed a wino sitting on a door stoop next door, his head nestled in his arms, undoubtedly asleep. Inside the restaurant was another drunk waving his arms and swearing in the strongest terms. Summoning the manager, I asked if he wanted to have the swearing drunk ejected. "Hell no, that's a customer," he exhorted. The manager wanted the sleeping wino removed.

The man in a diabetic quandry, angry because he couldn't get his car over the expressway divider, wherein his auto would be facing the speeding oncoming traffic.

The injured drunk who couldn't understand why he kept falling down, when he attempted to stand on his leg, which had a double compound fracture.

How about the guy who left the tavern to wait for a bus, returning in about ten minutes to sit down at the bar again and order a drink. After taking a swig, he fell to the floor in a faint, with a pen knife protruding from his back. He had resisted being robbed in the bus stop and was stabbed in the back. Apparently he thought that called for a drink.

On another occasion, a guy walked into the same tavern with chartreuse paint all over his head and a long strand of seaweed over one shoulder. Figure that one out.

Rose's Record Shop—where the window and inside are stocked with shoes, not a record in sight.

One store had its front window painted on the inside; of course it was backwards on the outside. Must have been raining the day they painted that one.

One engineering genius had about 180 feet of hose running from his basement water source to a water cooled air conditioner that stood two feet from his sink on the second floor. Why tap the sink for your water source when you can run 180 feet of hose to the basement??!!!

Another, that probably graduated from the same engineering school, had used two-by-fours to further reinforce his rear door inside. Of course, the door opened outward.

One kid threw a firecracker into a partially filled gas can, thinking it would make a louder explosion. As he flew through the garage wall, he probably realized he was right.

Another dude devised a rather clever device which fired a .410 shotgun round. However, it had one fault, six inches was too short, and, in trying to maintain a better grip on the device, he very cleverly placed his thumb over the muzzle. His victim, suffering from a shotgun wound to the head, and the shotgunner's thumb, were found at the scene. How's that for a print.

Another individual that had been burglarized several times, rigged a shotgun to fire at the burglar when he opened the basement door. Not the worst idea in the world, until the rigger, who happened to live above the basement, thought he heard a noise below. Frantically he ran downstairs and pulled open the basement door. The last I heard was that he would survive the effects of the shotgun wound. Well, at least his idea worked.

One woman called the police and, in a very indignant manner, related how the man in an apartment across the way was constantly parading completely nude in front of his window. "As a matter of fact," she said in an emphatic tone, "he's doing it now." Scanning the apartment building in question, the patrolman said, "Where, I don't see anyone." To that, the offended woman said, "Here, stand on this chair and you will."

Then there are the occasional odd jobs that policemen do. Ever present at parades, elections, sporting events, social events, schools and dozens of locations you would never expect a cop to be. Sometimes assigned to capture stray dogs, cats, possums, and all forms of escaped livestock. One new policeman, not knowing better, tried to get a bat that was flying around a woman's apartment. After shooting six holes in her ceiling and walls, he realized a bat's erratic flight makes an impossible target. If bats laugh, this one probably did, as he flew out an open window to escape.

Another hapless policeman was assigned to check on "snakes in the sewer." He probably thought it was an unfunny prank call, until he lifted the sewer cover to find three snakes just as surprised as he. The police department's animal unit would handle these creatures.

All too often we would receive calls of "Man exposing himself," in police parlance called a "wand waver." These sickies are undoubtedly under the misapprehension that it pays to advertise. Apparently they weren't aware that, for some women, even complete possession of such a marvelous instrument could fail to tickle their fancy. But, by some strange coincidence, police vehicles always seemed to be closer and more abundant in responding to the much lesser calls of "Woman exposing herself." I guess they just couldn't believe it.

"Dynamite on the front lawn." Couldn't be, but it was. Two sticks of dynamite, origin unknown. I actually saw the officer carrying the dynamite into the station. Little misjudgment there, but that's alright. The captain, seeing the potential danger, put it in his desk drawer. But he wasn't too slow. Two minutes later he left the station for lunch. Not returning 'til the bomb and arson unit had recovered the explosives. Some people thought they saw a kangaroo hopping around the northwest section of the city. Undoubtedly they did! After actually seeing some of these incidents, were I to receive a call of *Tyrannosaurus rex* on Main Street, I would simply check out a shotgun. After all, *tyrannosaurus rex* is a pretty big animal.

Midnights and Cold Food

Everyone else was now asleep. The refreshing shave had brought me back a little, but I still felt weary. As I dressed into the fresh uniform and strapped on the gunbelt, I wished I could reverse the procedure and steal into the warm bed, cuddling up to my wife, who was beautifully asleep.

After downing the remaining cup of cold coffee, I methodically loaded my service revolver. Six rounds—I hoped I wouldn't have to use. Quietly I closed the front door, making sure it was locked securely.

Traffic on the expressway was fairly light; the district station would be only fifteen minutes away. Soon I would be in a police vehicle, out in the world of night people. Midnights were a bitch! If you were a policeman for fifty years you could never get used to the midnight shift. For the first few hours, you could function fairly well, then the glare of lights, irritating your already tired eyes, plus the strain of trying to see in dark alleys or areas where something might be happening, started to take its toll. The constant patrolling and the time between assignments, all combining to sap your energy. An occasional cup of coffee helped, but man is not nocturnal and pretty soon you're in kind of a daze. This is a dangerous time for policemen, since your actions or reactions being subdued, could cause you to make a serious mistake . . . it has happened.

Knowing this, you try to be more careful, especially because the night brings out the weirdos, the types only psychiatrists seem to understand. Peeping Toms, rapists, child molesters . . . Jack the Rippers, the darkness of their minds stimulated by the night. Four o'clock, at least all the taverns were now closed. That would eliminate some potential violence. As we passed a large apartment building, the windows which had previously been dark, were now partially lit up in a staggered checkerboard fashion. Even the calls on the police radio started to increase . . . society was awakening.

Finally, the dove grey dawn, gently preparing your eyes for the soon to follow bright sunrise. Now, dog tired, you shuffled into some ham-and-egger. Everyone around you would be chipper and witty. The usual cute comments which you would try to answer with a smile. Pulling into the district lot and putting your equipment in your personal car was followed by checking out at the desk. One mover . . . one curfew . . . one arrest . . . or whatever.

Then you were on your way home. Most of the teeming expressway traffic would be going the other way; their day was just starting. Arriving at the house, as the curb ruthlessly shortened the life of the car's tires. Ignition off, my head slowly drooped down in exhaustion. At home, the kids were leaving for school. "Bye, Daddy." Sometimes I just flopped on the couch, without undressing . . . in sixteen hours it would start all over.

I glanced at my watch, 3:30 A.M. . . . Carl was still half asleep. "Think I'll go for coffee, Carl; you can stay in the car and catch a few minutes of sleep." Upon entering the all-night restaurant, I used the washroom, where the reflection in the mirror stared back with sleepy eyes. Sitting down at the counter, I wondered how long before one of the many insomniacs sitting there would invade my privacy with some stupid question or start a conversation. A middle-aged waitress came over. "See that street over there," she indicated across the way. "The street lights are out in the parking lot; you can always see the cars in the parking lot at night." She didn't care about the lights, the lot, or anything else; she just wanted to talk. "Oh, really!" I uttered in a manner that let her know I wasn't going to run out of the restaurant to change light bulbs. Never fails, some inconsiderate person always had to spoil your meal or coffee break. Lately I took a magazine or other reading matter when I went for lunch or coffee. When the mopes saw you reading, they usually assumed you wouldn't like to be interrupted—thank God. All night restaurants attract the insomniacs like moths to a flame. They want to talk to someone . . . anyone. They don't care if your food is getting cold or that you only get a half hour to eat—half that time waiting for your food. And, as they're bending your ear with their total nonsense, spittle is landing on your food. Of course, the mope has eaten his meal already and has nothing better to do but spoil yours. In the interest of public relations, policemen are obliged to overlook these idiots, but I was compelled to put this in the book since it is one of a policeman's frequent irritations. The next time you see a policeman or any uniformed person eating in a restaurant, leave the man alone to enjoy his meal.

Returning to the squad car, Carl asked, "Did you enjoy it?" "There aren't too many ways you can screw up tea," I answered. We resumed patrol.

Winter

Winter was a new ball game. It presented more new problems in doing the job. Calls for police service are fewer, one reason being because people drink less booze during the winter months. Domestic disturbance calls increase because people are home constantly and too much togetherness can be aggravating. There is more fault finding, bickering and fewer avenues to expend one's energies. Street crimes lessen, since criminals get just as cold as anyone else . . . plus there are fewer people on the street.

Getting to an assignment with dispatch is tricky, due to the very hazardous driving conditions. A chase can be pure prayer time. Some of the fair weather crossing guards seem to disappear with winter's bitter wind and cold. Most of these women are dedicated to their flocks of children, but some let their dedication drop with the temperature. So like many other jobs, in no way requiring an armed trained policeman, we found ourselves filling the gap. A total misuse of police manpower. The men assigned to three-wheel motorcycles, for traffic enforcement, also had some difficulties brought about by winter. Staying warm, not being the least. Ballpoint pens freeze up in winter and the department graciously allowed the use of pencils in writing tickets.

Derelicts who slept outside in the warmer months

now must find places of shelter to survive. Many looked forward to the baloney sandwich and warmth of the district lockup. Some were found dead, frozen stiff, under porches, homemade shelters, or wherever they may have lain down to sleep. Some burned to death, trying to keep warm by an open fire. Frostbite also took its toll. About the only good thing snow and cold weather in the city brought was Christmas. Even the usual low morale of most policemen got a lift. We sometimes had a choice of either Christmas or New Year's Eve to be off duty. Anybody that got both sure wasn't just a patrolman. The cold, clear weather sharpened your senses, and, with your eyes closed, you could tell by various odors, what street or section of the district you were passing. What a wonderful scent from the bakery, or the clean smell from the commercial laundry. One company manufactured incense. The railroad areas, or the elevated structure on Lake Street, had as distinct an odor as any. Probably the garden spot of the district was Humboldt Park, where, as a boy, I had spent many carefree days. The beautiful symmetry of its leafless trees had to be one of God's finest works. And who could deny the absolute majesty of those same trees with a velvet coat of snow glistening in the moonlight. Maybe the district wasn't so bad during winter, after all. Even the old snow-covered frame buildings had a timeless charm of their own.

Whenever I was near the railroad areas, the lonesome train whistles and smell of diesel trains took me back to earlier times and other places. I could get quite maudlin, but not for long. The police radio would bring you back in a second. "Man with a gun—use caution!" We were on our way, rear wheels slippin' and slidin' on winter's reluctant pavement.

Summer

Beer and fire hydrants both freely flow during the hot summer months. The poor kids' wading pools were gutters filled with the very cold water that issued forth from the illegally opened hydrants. Most would splash around in the refreshing water, wearing their street clothes. Whatever attempt made to secure the hydrants, like steel collars that deterred the use of pipe wrenches, was overcome by the ingenious youths. When instructed to turn the hydrants off, we would drive by fifteen minutes later to find them reopened. As far as the kids were concerned, an open hydrant was the greatest.

As the weather got hotter, the consumption of beer increased. People would sit in front of their apartment houses drinking cans of beer to the blaring sounds from portable radios. Most would stay peaceful, too hot to get physical. A few would become boisterous, or start fights.

Disturbance calls in taverns increased due to the volume of people drinking alcohol to slake their thirst. The weather in Chicago during summer isn't just hot, it's humid, muggy, polluted and most uncomfortable. Even the nights stay hot and for those without an air conditioner, getting a good night's sleep could be a real challenge.

The district station had a few fans and the captain's office had an air conditioner. But, other than roll call, or bringing in a prisoner, we wouldn't be in the station too long. None of the police vehicles had air and riding around in them for eight hours wearing woolen trousers was the ultimate in discomfort. Why the police department never switched to khakis for the hot weather always did boggle my mind. Too logical, I guess. If you were involved in a fight or had to carry a two hundred pound stiff, sweat would ooze from every pore. What a pleasure to splash cold water on your face and upper body after work, then change to a fresh dress shirt and slacks. Most of the guys changed after work, the locker room smelling like a whore's bedroom, from the aftershave and other preparations. Many would stop for a cool brew before going home. Another full house for Demi's, our favorite gin mill. When we were patroling during the hot weather, we would drive to the factory area and park the car in the shade, doors wide open, engine shut off.

Some squad cars were called shield cars. They had a plexiglass window dividing the front seat from the rear. This gave the driver and his partner little room for air to circulate. The prisoner section, with windows up and inside handles removed, was a real hot box. Usually couldn't stay parked for too long; the police radio would see to that.

Would you believe as I wrote the above line, the squad operator just assigned us to a job. Upon our arrival, a man came over to the car, "He's laying on the grass in back of this building." "Who?" we asked. Our job had nothing to do with anybody lying anywhere. After locking up the car, we walked to the rear of the building. Sure enough, there was a black man lying on the grass. His left leg was broken, the bloody bone protruding through his skin just above the ankle. Apparently he had jumped over a four foot fence and landed the wrong way. He was wearing those stupid high-soled type shoes which he now jokingly offered to anybody in the small crowd of gawkers for three dollars. For some reason, he was not in extreme pain, but the sight of that jagged, bloody bone made me feel uneasy. He was placed, wincing, in the ambulance and we now were on our way to the hospital, where our injured man would be taken. Our original job had been reassigned. At the air-conditioned hospital we would make out the necessary form, then resume patrol.

Sometimes you would end up doing something totally different from what you were assigned. Like some officer once quipped, "This is the only district I ever worked where you locked up the victims." But that's police work . . . totally unpredictable.

Gut Instinct

The weather had been muggy, but now it began to rain lightly. I drove the squad car up an incline and onto railroad property. My partner sat silently, his eyes closed. An occasional train slowly passed through the yard. As the patter of rain on the squad car roof increased, the grey sky darkened in color. Looking out over the railroad yard, I remembered all the other times I had been there. It was a good place to take a break and perhaps reflect on previous events. The railroad yard was one of my favorite spots. It seemed to have a personality which changed with the seasons. Ever present was the odor of creosote, the chemical used to preserve railroad ties, and all the other odors associated with trains. On a few occasions, we fired our .38's, just to make sure they were still functioning.

Our beat number was called and my partner sleepily acknowledged the assignment. We headed towards the job, windshield wiper thumping as we drove through the now heavy rainfall. Since I had passed the age of thirty-five, locations, things, and people seemed to take on more depth and dimension. I could even perceive a mood at different times, whereas previously, everything seemed to be for the moment. Lately, I would hang around the police station after my tour of duty, talking to the guys on the other watch, or just observing the whole scene. When I was younger, leaving the station for home, a gin mill, or whatever, seemed to be imperative. Now time seemed to slow down, or was it me?

Getting back to moods and perceptions . . . once, while patroling in a one-man car I passed a given intersection. Nothing overly different about it, but a powerful overwhelming sense or feeling of something not right. Describing the feeling isn't possible, but it was there. I actually drove around the block three times. Two times, that ominous feeling increased when I passed a corner where several young people were enjoying themselves at a refreshment stand. Nothing appeared to be wrong. The third time around a car just in front of me pulled to the curb and two men jumped out. One of the men leveled a pump shotgun at the group of people by the stand. His buddy nervously looking over his shoulder, spotted my squad car. He immediately warned his friend and in a moment they were back in their car, hurriedly disassembling the shotgun. I snapped on the Mars Light and pulled the squad car in front of them to prevent their escape. In seconds, assist cars arrived in response to my 10-1 (officer needs help). Approaching the two men with our guns drawn, they surrendered meekly. In their haste to disassemble the shotgun, they had left a round in the chamber. It was no hoax or attempt to scare—they were intent upon killing. It happened so fast, I don't think some of the group at the refreshment stand were ever aware of the incident.

The feelings I experienced preceding that incident have always eluded definition for me. Was it premonition, intuition, or gut instinct? As time went by, I seemed to be able to "feel" a situation that had any real danger. Whether a traffic stop or an in-progress call. Most policemen develop this instinct to their advantage. Some that didn't aren't here anymore . . .

The New Kids

The new kids were always full of energy and drove continuously. Hard to recall yourself being that same young anxious talkative lad. I didn't really like to work with the new kids. They drove too fast to see anything on patrol and much too fast responding to calls of no emergency. Most were nice guys trying to do their best, but good policemen are the product of time, maturity and experience. This takes many years, not weeks or months. One donkey with less than a month on the street told me his star was as big as mine. I'm sure by now, he realizes, not as bright. Over the years I have met some men I helped break in on the job that are now fine policemen. That's very satisfying to me. The advice of the old timer is still invaluable; it might save your life!

Here's one young policeman's definition of what he thinks policemen are: recorders of crime, dog catchers, marriage counselors, pimps for the insurance companies, and all-around bad guys. In ten more years, he wouldn't believe he said that. The narrowness of his thinking will have been replaced by understanding.

Police work demands youthful vigor and the experience of time. Nothing less than a blend will do. Like the newly married husband told his wife, "Here, put my trousers on." She did, exclaiming that they were too big. "That's right," the husband said. "That's to show you who the boss is." "Oh, really," the wife said. "Try my panties on." The husband couldn't get them on past his knees. "I can't get into your pants," he admitted. "That's right," his clever wife said, "and you're not going to until your attitude changes."

Attitude in police work or any other is most important. Formulation of a harmonious, productive attitude would take time to mellow, as does fine wine. By and large, most new men were chomping at the bit to save society from the cancer of wrongdoers. No task too unconquerable. They were policemen and would prove their worth. The overabundance of zeal was like a shot of adrenaline. Even the older men like myself made the contrast evident. But we knew, if you ran up a flight of stairs, your energy was wasted on the stairs. Or, once you squeezed the trigger, the bullet was irretrievable. The headlines wouldn't say, "Heroic policeman shoots dangerous felon." They would say "Cop kills kid!"

For a policeman coming on the job today, society had slipped a noose around his neck. Every son of a bitch is sick, not a felon, and more and more found "not guilty." As time goes by, policemen might even find themselves saying, "Sir, may I please have that shotgun; due to your illness you robbed that storekeeper and blew his head off." And, if he says, "No," maybe they'll have to let him go. In reality, police departments are at the mercy of the public. They must satisfy needs and demands. Not necessarily in that order. Ironically, the law would limit the police department's effectiveness. While policemen pondered whether they had all the elements for a lawful arrest, the bastard would simply run away. But, just as soon as the police wrest the gun or knife away from a murderer, heaven forbid they should forget to tell him his rights. And beware of riots; everybody knows who starts them. So what if you get hurt or shot; policemen get paid to take risks. Besides, the guy who did it is sick. Most

101

police functions have become more legally intricate. For the new men, the job would be a much greater challenge. Many of the new men have better educations, which is decidedly to their advantage. Maturity and time would shape the new men into fine officers.

And soon the stars they wear will have become as big and bright as any that had preceded.

Police Wives

Isn't that clever! Starts with the new men, ends with the new men. Kind of literally artistic. I thought the book was finished. What else really needed to be said? Hadn't I told of the heroics, the danger, the drinking? Hadn't I been realistically honest? Did I miss something? I, like some policemen, had unintentionally overlooked an extremely important part of our lives . . . the women. How could I have been so blind . . . so insensitive . . . so stupid. Who would suffer the brunt of a policeman's frustrations? Who is closest? His mother, girl friend, wife. Usually a wife . . . divorce statistics of policemen would prove that. I, like some policemen whether egocentric or just plain stupid, had never really realized the traumatic impact on our spouses.

After a few drinks at another joint . . . now closed, I migrated to Joe's, a four o'clock joint. In good spirits, I entered joking with Joe and two unescorted women sitting at the bar. In a friendly lighthearted way, we discussed frivolous subjects. I never suspected the innocent conversation would gravitate to the stark reality of policemen and their wives. The one girl had a short hair style, which in my less than sober reasoning opened a door towards long hair and femininity. So we joked around that and other subjects, only to discover that we could relate to each other quite openly. The young lady would in time tell me of her relationship through marriage to a policeman. Not a sob story, not a fabrication. But an earnest revelation of the difficulties involved for a woman married to a policeman. In her particular case they had married at a very tender age . . . childhood sweethearts. At best a difficult challenge . . . however, surmountable. Then her husband had become a policeman. Were he to have become anything else, they still might not have made it. But I knew down deep, only the strongest bond between any husband and wife could weather this new lifestyle. They both worked and, as time went by, saw less of each other. His job so demanding . . . no room or time on his hectic schedule for anyone else. Weekends, holidays, even normal working hours, being alien to a policeman's rotating shifts. Each year, thirteen twenty-eight day shifts—called periods, going around the clock in eight-hour segments. Police families would have to adjust to this new calendar and the abnormal hours. Some regular days off diabolically assigned to traffic court. Any other court appearances having no regard for his personal life or obligations. Despite all, he loved the job. The danger, adventure, the non-routine hours. But how about her? How about the normalcy of a weekend as a family. Their husband-wife relationship . . . their life together. In time the different hours, and the growing distance his job had created took its toll. In time he would find solace with other women. He might have anyway, were he not a policeman . . . but not as easily.

Due to the constantly changing shifts, his metabolism had become unstable; frustration would manifest itself. While she slept he would be wide awake, drinking and susceptible to the lure of other women. Unaware, he would fall into the trap; that in time would dissolve their marriage. With no ill intent he was merely the victim of a job that could ruthlessly, in a slow subtle manner overcome those not supremely individually strong. Their lives now opposed, were in conflict. How flexible could she be? How much should she take? How much could she take without losing her self-respect?

I had been on the treadmill for many years, managing my home life and the job fairly well. But many times it was a frustrating challenge. How do your measure job security against the abnormal life situation it fostered. Which was more important, a steady pay check or the problems it created? As she related her personal story, I couldn't help but reflect on my own situation. Did my wife suffer a similar purgatory all these years? Was she strong enough to endure, or weak enough to submit? Little doubt that most of the wives kept their fears and anguish within. Why burden the husbands with their anxieties? Would it really help for him to know of the sleepless nights? While he patrolled the streets and alleys, giving security to others, he might lose his own. Couldn't really blame the job; it was just a fact of life. As a man, you are supposed to be able to handle it and yourself. After working the third shift, you didn't have to party 'til four in the morning. With all the negatives, the job could be a reason . . . but never an excuse. As time went by, you would take your wife out less frequently. After all, you were out all the time.

I remember coming home at five or six in the morning once, and, as I undressed, my wife sleepily looked up and asked, "Why are you getting up so early; going somewhere?" She wasn't even aware that I was out all night.

During the riots we worked a minimum of twelve hours, being released as the situation dictated. How could a wife plan dinner or any social event, not knowing at any given time when you were coming home . . . sometimes fearing never. The husband could lose his frustrations in alcohol or in the arms of another woman, but how about the wives? How about their wants, their needs . . . their love.

Epilogue

Hopefully this book has helped some people gain more of an insight into what policemen see and do. At least this is the way one policeman saw it. Not always clean and good, or dirty and bad, but most of the things people are capable of. Truth is definitely stranger than fiction—any cop knows that to be a fact. Some police units aren't mentioned in the book, simply because I didn't work in them and couldn't honestly tell of their deeds. It was not my intention to minimize their efforts, certainly they also are worthy of the highest praise. My reason for writing this book was to tell it like it is.

As time goes by, the facts dim and so does your ardor. All too soon you look into a mirror and see that the young man is gone, the gray hair and a few lines have replaced the once bashful grin. Your memories have become a collage of experiences. But the story had to be told. Not a Hollywood version, boob tube exploitation, or literary work of art. The men who have sworn an oath to protect your life, even at the cost of losing their own, deserve better. At the very least, they deserve a little more understanding.